OAKLAND COMMUNITY COLLEGE

3 2355 00153735 6

D1483370

Banton

QH
367
.B34

Darwinism and the study
of society

Oakland Community College
Highland Lakes Library
7350 Cooley Lake Road
Union Lake, Michigan

DARWINISM AND THE STUDY OF SOCIETY

Darwinism
and
The Study of Society

A CENTENARY SYMPOSIUM

With contributions by

MICHAEL BANTON, S. A. BARNETT,
TOM BURNS, B. FARRINGTON,
MORRIS GINSBERG, LANCELOT HOGBEN,
GEORGE SHEPPERSON, J. MAYNARD SMITH,
W. STARK, C. H. WADDINGTON, BASIL WILLEY

Edited by

Michael Banton

With an Introduction by
J. BRONOWSKI

LONDON: TAVISTOCK PUBLICATIONS
CHICAGO: QUADRANGLE BOOKS

First published in 1961
in Great Britain
by Tavistock Publications (1959) Limited
11 New Fetter Lane, London E.C.4

First published in 1961
in the United States of America
by Quadrangle Books, Inc.
119 W. Lake Street, Chicago, Illinois

© *Michael Banton, 1961*
with the exception of 'Darwinism and Human Society
in Retrospect' © *Lancelot Hogben, 1961*

Library of Congress Catalog Card Number 61-7932

Printed in Great Britain
in 10 point Times Roman by
C. Tinling & Co., Ltd., Liverpool, London, and Prescot

Contents

Contents

Editor's Preface

These essays are based upon papers read at a conference held at the University of Edinburgh, 8th-10th April, 1959. The holding of the conference was originally proposed by the Scottish Branch of the British Sociological Association; the arrangements committee consisted of Sir Hector Hetherington (Chairman), James Drever (Vice-Chairman), S. A. Barnett, Tom Burns, H. G. Callan, John Highet, A. L. Macfie, D. M. Mackinnon, A. D. Ritchie, S. A. Sklaroff, C. H. Waddington, W. P. D. Wightman and Michael Banton (Secretary).

Thanks are due to Ernest Benn Limited for permission to reproduce an extract from *The Place of Prejudice in Modern Civilisation*, by Sir Arthur Keith; and to Oliver & Boyd Limited in respect of *Scottish Democracy, 1815–1840*, by L. J. Saunders.

J. BRONOWSKI
Introduction

One merit of the subject of this book is that it is fresh. *Darwinism and the Study of Society* is not an examination topic, nor does it fit ready-made into an established academic field. There are no set rules to say how the theme shall be treated, and there are not even many precedents. Therefore the authors of the essays that follow have had to find their own way, and this not only in detail but in their very conception of the subject. Each author has had to weigh the two parts of the title himself, *Darwinism* and *The Study of Society*, and to judge for himself where the centre of gravity of the two parts falls. As a result, what each author has written is as interesting in revealing his total outlook, his imaginative vision of the mechanism of society, as in the more formal matter which he presents.

Because each author has interpreted the subject afresh, their essays range widely. At one end, the range touches on Charles Darwin's most personal thoughts, his scruples about religion, for example, which Professor Basil Willey and Mr. George Shepperson both recall. At the other end lies, say, the subtle system of connections which must exist if the totality of an animal's evolutionary traits is to form a stable and self-perpetuating unity, which Professor C. H. Waddington discusses. If I were to try in this Introduction to build a mosaic of all these different approaches, I should succeed only in making a minia-ture blur, for ideas so diverse cannot be treated in summary. What I shall do instead is to focus on two or three preoccupations, the two or three common points of view, which run through most of the essays. By drawing attention to these common assumptions at the beginning, I hope that I can prepare the reader to ask questions of the essays as he reads them and to see how far the book as a whole answers his unwritten questions.

Introduction

The first thing that strikes me about these essays is a point of interpretation: the interpretation of the word *Darwinism* in the title. Charles Robert Darwin called the book that he published in 1859 *On the Origin of Species by Means of Natural Selection.* His book, then, is about the origin of species: its central subject, the revolutionary thought in it, is that new, true species can be formed at all. Natural selection does come into Darwin's title, but it comes in only at the tail. To treat natural selection as the major content of *The Origin of Species* is to let the tail wag the title, and make the explanation of the subject more important than the subject itself. We ought not to think of Darwin's work as if it were devoted to describing the rivalry between individuals for the resources of nature. Still less ought we to think of it as describing the rivalry between species, as if the balance between species or other groups were a kind of warfare. When Darwin called his book *The Origin of Species*, he did not mean to write either *Competition in Nature* or *The Rivalry of Species.*

The reader should therefore beware of the temptation, to which many sociologists yield, to make Darwinism stand only for a mechanism of social struggle. The temptation is often present in the essays that follow, and its acceptance shows how much less profound the concepts of sociology still are than those of biology. Dr. W. Stark indeed limits his discussion of 'Natural and Social Selection' to an account of some nineteenth-century writers who interpreted social evolution as a struggle for power between rivals, and who justified this interpretation by their reading of Darwin. But in fact, this is an excessively simple reading, and it is not surprising that the authors whom Dr. Stark parades have been forgotten.

What does surprise me is that Dr. Stark's authors (and other sociologists since then) should have gone to Darwin at all for their simple conception. For just as we know, as a matter of science, that this is not the whole of Darwin's thought, so we also know, as a matter of history, that this conception is not original in Darwin. The idea that nature is kept in balance by a struggle between individuals, in which the weakest goes to the wall, is much older than *The Origin of Species*. It was original in the eighteenth, not in the nineteenth century; indeed, it had the power of a doctrine among eighteenth-century rationalists. Daniel Defoe and Jonathan Swift are full of it, almost a hundred years before Charles Darwin was born. More than a hundred years before Darwin was born, in 1705, Bernard de Mandeville had made it the theme of a book which, when he later reprinted it as *The Fable of the Bees*, became a classic guide for eighteenth-century educators.

The Fable of the Bees was written to show, as a parable, that social competition among the bees exactly contrives to keep the hive in balance. To point this moral, Mandeville gave it the telling sub-title *Private Vices, Public Benefits*. This phrase summarises the dominant intellectual theory of the eighteenth century, that the health of society positively requires the weakest to go to the wall. The giving of charity, and particularly the education of the poor, were actively condemned, because it was held that we disturb the dynamic balance of society if we interfere by helping the weaklings.

In short, long before Darwin, eighteenth-century writers were already full of warnings that a society which protects its less successful members will find itself burdened by them, and in the end over-burdened. This is also what Dr. Stark's authors feared in the nineteenth century; and it remains the main talking point of critics of the Welfare State in the twentieth century. Usually the critics in our own century warn us that there is a moral weakness, a lack of fibre, which will spread through our society like an infection if we do not eliminate those who have failed to get to the top. The assumption is, of course, that they have failed to get to the top because they suffer from moral weakness.

But there are also critics now who believe that our society is threatened by the spread of more tangible handicaps. Consider, for example, the school of educators who are preoccupied with the idea of the average intelligence of a population, and who for thirty years or so were led by the late Sir Godfrey Thomson. This school argues that because the average intelligence quotient of a large family of children is lower than that of a small family, the intelligence of the population as a whole must be falling. On the surface, this argument looks plausible; but two massive surveys of the schoolchildren of Scotland have now shown that the facts do not support it. On the contrary, the more recent survey discloses a significant rise in the average intelligence quotient. It would give me pleasure if I could record, in this Introduction to a series of essays first presented at Edinburgh, that those who made the two surveys of intelligence in Scotland had followed the example of other scientists who see that their predictions are at fault. That is, I should like to be able to say that the surveyors had re-examined their original argument—which in fact is open to several criticisms. Alas, they have not; this is not the method of the doctrinal followers of Mandeville's thesis on education. The only thing that the second survey of the schoolchildren of Scotland tries to argue out of existence is the fact—the fact that their average intelligence quotient is higher. Evidently this school of educators finds the fact unwelcome.

THE SURVIVAL OF THE FITTEST

Professor Lancelot Hogben in his essay gives other examples of the readiness with which those who want to justify the status of their own group seize upon measurements, particularly of brain and intelligence, which are supposed to show that a rival group is inferior by nature. There is a touch of distress and indignation in their attitude: the distress that we used to sense in Sir Godfrey Thomson's evident disquiet at the thought that manual workers have large families. But more even than indignation, there is the ambition to justify the position of advantage which the research worker himself holds. He wants to prove that nature selected him for success, not by chance, but because he was better fitted to succeed. If there is any merit in the phrase 'the survival of the fittest', it is that the survivors can at least use it as proof of their own fitness.

I have criticised one reading of Darwin as being too simple: the view that human societies are kept in balance simply by a struggle for power—a struggle mainly between individuals. The phrase 'the survival of the fittest' is a little less crude than this. It implies that there are grounds for survival, and that nature or society, in getting rid of the failures, is judging them by some permanent test. Fitness must represent a permanent choice, not merely between individuals but between continuing groups; for individuals do not live long enough for their survival to be of lasting importance. When we talk of survival, we must mean the survival of a self-perpetuating group.

Yet even with this gloss, I find the phrase 'the survival of the fittest' rather shallow, and that for several reasons. First, in every practical example, any test of fitness that we apply (other than the test of survival, which begs the question) seems to me very dubious. Take the delightful example quoted by Mr. S. A. Barnett: babies in their early months develop the habit of smiling when they see a human face. Are we then to believe that this smile confers a survival value on those men and women who had it as babies? Mr. Barnett is of course scrupulous to produce some evidence that the life of a baby is sometimes easier for having this social smile. 'It has been reported in the United States,' he writes (cautiously if not sceptically), 'that mothers who had at first been rather cool towards their offspring often underwent a marked change of feeling when social smiling began.' But are we really to believe that this advantage gives the baby a flying start for the rest of its life? Do men who softened their mothers' hearts as babies in fact go on to have more children than those who did not? Can we credit that populations in which the babies smile have a larger number of adult survivors than populations in which the babies do not smile? Such questions cannot be answered with anything that counts for evidence in biology. And in the social sciences, the only assurance which a writer can put into his answer is self-assurance.

Second, if the fittest members of a species survive to form its stock, should not the same competition also go on between the species themselves? We know that some species are very numerous, and that others have died out. Should not nature have got rid of the less numerous species at a much greater pace before now? We cannot readily believe that all the surviving species are equally well fitted to their environment. But if they are not, how do the less well-fitted survive? Why, in fact, is the world not peopled by a single species which has a marginal advantage over all others?

The answer, of course, is that fitness for an environment must mean something more subtle and more flexible than mere mechanical adaptation. Fitness must contain factors which make for some diversity, so that the species is not snuffed out by every minor disturbance in the environment. Fitness must also include an integration of parts, a pattern of hereditary factors which hold together— and this pattern itself must be stable under the fluctuations of the environment. Nature acknowledges this need for the factors of heredity to form integrated patterns by the very fact that she ties the genes together on the chromosomes. But there must also be more plastic and delicate assemblies of hereditary factors: the patterns without which the organism cannot function as a whole, to which Professor C. H. Waddington has pointed in his thoughtful essay. To my mind, the physical resemblances between some of the Old World mammals and their New World analogues must derive from the necessary evolution of patterns of this kind. And at a simpler level, such phenomena as the symmetry of most animals seem to me equally to point to the existence of some essential basic patterns.

These are biological topics, and they show how profound are the concepts of Darwinism today. We cannot be content to accept less subtle concepts in the social sciences. How can we suppose that 'the survival of the fittest' works more crudely in man's adaptations to his societies than in an animal's adaptation to its whole environment? Animals have many ways of coming to terms with a changing environment. The coelacanth did not, after all, die in the struggle against its more modern rivals in the upper sea. The coelacanth retreated to the deep ocean, and has survived there happily for millions of years. What an animal species survives by in the end is not adaptation but adaptability. The most striking evidence for this is indeed the evolution of the human race itself. For the instrument which has driven our headlong success is the human brain; and the brain is not an adaptation, but a wonderfully complex store of adaptability. In particular, because the human brain goes on working well long after the body does not, it has been able to act as a store for adaptations which cannot be passed on by heredity.

This brings me to the third difficulty which the phrase 'the survival of the fittest' raises in the social sciences. In biology, a species ensures its survival by the fertility of its members. An individual may be superbly fitted to the environment (and to future environments), but if he or she is not fertile, their fitness is lost to the species. Even though the mammals are less spendthrift in this than, say, the fishes and the insects, fertility remains a basic condition for their evolution. However, and in sharp contrast, human societies perpetuate themselves quite differently—by gaining control over their environment (including their rivals). Alexander the Great spread Greek culture to the ends of the known earth, but not because his family, or even his Greek following, was large. King Solomon seems to have been very fertile, but he did not owe his influence to that. Isaac Newton had no children, yet he changed the course of human development more than any other man.

Alexander, Solomon and Newton turned the evolution of man in new directions in a way in which no animal can change its evolution. This is the nature of social evolution, and it may be that individuals who create outstanding social or technical changes play as radical a part in it as mutants play in biological evolution. It has indeed been suggested that the unit of social evolution is a new invention, just as the unit of biological evolution is the gene. But the fact is that we know almost nothing about this, even if we interpret the word 'invention' to include every kind of social innovation. The fact is that we have not begun to look for the units of social change.

We have not begun to look for the units of social change, and we cannot look for them until we study the correlated changes that go together in societies. This is what I miss in discussions of social evolution at present: the sense that there are units of change to be found, and to be found by a method of correlation. The question, what units hang together and what units fail to hold together, has hardly been broached in sociology. Yet this is the crucial field of study in biology today, as Professor Waddington's essay shows; and it is also a crucial field in physics. In physics we know, at least empirically, what arrangements of protons and neutrons hang together to make nuclei; and we have long known what arrangements of atoms hang together to make molecules, and what arrangements do not hold together. In biology we are at this moment discovering how the atoms of inheritance, the genes, hang together to form what I will call molecular arrangements—that is, the stable constituents of the gene complex. But in the social sciences, we know neither the units nor their stable arrangements.

THE UNIT OF INHERITANCE

I have passed from 'the survival of the fittest' to the concept of the gene complex, because without that the idea of fitness in biology is hopelessly shallow. But the gene complex, which is a conception of the mid-twentieth century, has its roots in the discovery of the gene, which belongs to the threshold of this century. Here lies the precise crux of Darwinism; and it is the neglect of this crux which makes me criticise the reach-me-down interpretations of Darwin, the old commonplaces of sociology that go back to the eighteenth century. The single most important thing that Charles Darwin did was to force biologists to find a unit of inheritance—even though Darwin was dead before biologists recognised what had been found.

When Darwin published *The Origin of Species* in 1859, his achievement was at once recognised for what it was: an appealing solution to the puzzle, how living things come to be at the same time so diverse and yet so much alike. Darwin's readers felt that his solution carried conviction, even when they felt all the more strongly that they must resist the conviction. Intellectually, *The Origin of Species* made sense; even Darwin's opponents knew that; and as a result, it polarised opposition and conviction so powerfully that the spread of its logic, which might have taken a century, was packed into a decade or two. *The Origin of Species* made sense; everyone could see that life might indeed have moved and changed by these steps; everyone could see that the tree of life might indeed be a family tree. The religious opponents and the agnostic supporters could both see that if the tree of life had a single family trunk, and if adaptation by natural selection caused that trunk to branch, then both the differences and the likenesses between living things were understandable.

So far, the general reader of Darwin could go; and only the professional biologists did not stop there, and wanted to go farther. They granted that adaptation could account for the branching of the family tree; truth to tell, they had already granted almost as much to Charles

Introduction

Darwin's grandfather, Erasmus Darwin, in the eighteenth century. But now they asked a sharper question: If adaptation works by natural selection, what is the material on which natural selection works? What is the origin of the variations without which no branching of the family tree can begin?

Darwin was aware of this pressing question, How does variation begin? and he knew that he could not answer it. This is one of the two reasons that made him reluctant to publish his work until Alfred Russel Wallace forced his hand. Darwin did not shirk the issue, and often underlines it in such phrases as 'variability, which seems to us in our ignorance to be spontaneous'. Moreover, Darwin also saw that he needed a mechanism of inheritance which must preserve and not smudge these variations; and he had no idea how this could be. If species have their origin in heritable variations between individuals, then the one thing that Darwin's book did not do was to explain the origin of species; for this requires a theory of variations and their inheritance which he did not have.

Thus the fundamental problem, the primeval problem as it were, which Darwin's wonderfully full record of the relation between species forced on the attention of biologists, came from a deeper layer than the workings of natural selection. The problem was, where in a collection of individuals is the pool of heritable variations on which natural selection can work? In short, where is the raw material which makes it possible for one species to evolve in one direction, and a second species to branch in another direction, from the same stock? And how is this pool replenished? For the pool must be replenished if evolution is still going on, for example in the domestic plants and animals.

I have called this the primeval problem set by *The Origin of Species*. Darwin did not solve it, although he knew that its solution depended in some way on the occurrence of what he called 'sports'. Yet the solution was not in sight when *The Origin of Species* was published, even though Gregor Johann Mendel was then about to begin, in an obscure corner of Europe remote from the flow of scientific debate, the experiments whose rediscovery after 1900 gave the key to the primeval problem. Even so, and even after 1900, genetics was torn by dissension between, roughly, those who believed in Mendel's isolation of Darwin's 'sports', and those who did not. These dissensions, for example between William Bateson and Karl Pearson in England, had all the ferocity of the more recent dissensions on the same theme in Russia between Vavilov and Lysenko.

All this was precipitated by *The Origin of Species*: by the irrepressible need which Darwin created to find a precise mechanism for inheritance. Natural selection, the struggle for survival, the survival of the fittest are very well as phrases to describe in general terms how an ill-defined welter of individuals produces a neutral and balanced state of nature. But if natural selection is to produce groups which are truly different and self-perpetuating, if natural selection is to produce species, then there must be underlying units on which natural selection can work. The discovery of these units, and the elucidation of the method of their inheritance, were forced on biology by Darwin's work. This mechanism is altogether more profound than the balancing mechanism in Mandeville's beehive which, alas, has continued to preoccupy the minds of educators from Isaac Watts onwards.

The study of society still suffers from our inability to find units of social variation which differentiate one group from another, one organisation from another—perhaps one society from another—and which can be passed on in a stable manner. We have not taken the step which Darwin forced on biologists: we have not found the units on which social selection works. Without these units, it is two centuries too late to go on talking about fitness and survival. The industrial and political society in which we live is both too complex and too supple for such general ideas to be useful to explain its continuing evolution. And it is clear that we can only find these units, as geneticists have done since Mendel began, by statistical means. We have to find correlations between those features of society which hang and move together. Unhappily, little of the work in the social sciences follows what seems to me this essential thread through their labyrinth. Yet this is the thread which I trace back to Darwin, and which I would have liked to see unravelled some way in a book of essays on *Darwinism and the Study of Society*.

THE ROLE OF CHANCE

There is a second illumination, equally bright, which *The Origin of Species* threw over the sciences—over all the sciences. Darwin saw that there must be certain fundamental variants, what he called 'sports', on which natural selection works. How does it work? By jostling and shuffling them about until some arrangement which they form branches off in an evolutionary direction of its own. But if natural selection works in this way, at random on a random set of variants, then evolution is at bottom a process of chance—and this, even if some random arrangements turn out to be stable and others unstable. The selection of stable sets of heritable variants to form species which are adapted to their environment (and to its fluctuations) is a gigantic wheel of chance. There is no guide to evolution, there is no direction in life, there is no drive other than the hazard of probabilities which happens to throw up one among many possible adaptations. The growth and progress of life, its more and more subtle organisation and complexity, all the way from the amoeba to the human brain, is the work of chance.

I think that we no longer understand how shocking this thought was to Darwin's contemporaries. What we understand now, what we dwell on, is that their religious feelings were outraged. They were indeed, but for simpler reasons. Religious minds were outraged to be told that man derives from the same stock as the animals, for there is no evidence in nature that man required a special and separate act of creation. We know that Darwin was troubled by the fear of offending religious minds, and particularly by the fear of offending his wife, which was the second ground that made him reluctant to publish his work. There is factual evidence for all this, even though Darwin was evasive when strangers asked him questions about religion. Professor Basil Willey is too kind to Darwin's contemporaries when he suggests that their religious feelings ought not to have been outraged, and that Darwin did not think that they should be. Things were much rougher in 1859. Educated men had been brought up in a tradition to which religion was integral; Darwin himself had been brought up in it. No hindsight can laugh off Darwin's scruples and delays, the draft of his theory written apologetically in pencil, and his declared distress at distressing his wife. Religious men may come to terms with *The Origin of Species* today because they must. In 1859 they did not think that they must, and no wise apologist could have persuaded them then that the book did not attack the special relation between God and man.

But what was equally shocking, what we no longer understand today, is that Darwin's work also attacked the special relation between God and his whole creation. For *The Origin of Species* attacked the sense of purpose in the creation, and in its place put an Epicurean dance of chance. All this went counter to the philosophy with which the nineteenth century sustained its religious sense. The triumph of the Calvinist outlook which John Wesley had preached, the decline of the mild deism of the eighteenth century which such liberal thinkers as Benjamin Franklin and Joseph Priestley had held, had also been a decisive victory for the Stoic philosophy over the Epicurean. These issues of Greek philosophy were taught as moral lessons in schools, and they were alive to educated men in 1859. The Epicurean philosophy had long been defeated; Democritus and his atoms were only a scientific fable for chemists; and the age believed what John Dryden in his most devout mood had written long before, that

> No Atoms casually together hurl'd
> Could e're produce so beautifull a world.

Now, suddenly, the prime mover in the cosmic process was revealed to be not purpose but chance. The shock was felt at once by men of searching intellect. We know from some of them, from Leslie Stephen for example, how deep was the effect it had. In time this became the second revolution of minds that *The Origin of Species* brought about.

Of course it is not impossible to believe in a God who uses evolution as his instrument. After all, Newton had believed in a God who uses gravitation as his instrument. Newton and later physicists had not thought that their belief in God was undermined because they also believed him to have laid down, and thereafter to be bound by, the laws of gravitation. But there remains a profound difference between a God who uses gravitation and a God who works by the chance processes of evolution. Gravitation is an orderly process, a clockwork to which the word 'law' is appropriate. By contrast, at any instant, chance is lawless and disorderly, and the God who uses it as his instrument is, in a phrase which Albert Einstein has since made famous, a God playing at dice. This is not a relation between God and his creation which the Stoics of the nineteenth century could accept.

The scientists who did accept this vision from *The Origin of Species* were the physicists. We know that this is so. We know, for example, that Ludwig Boltzmann so admired the book that he said in 1886 that the century would be remembered not as a century of physics but as the century of Darwin. Boltzmann became the founder of the statistical mechanics of atoms, in the modern sense. He laid bare the relation between the random movements of atoms on the small scale and their law-abiding behaviour on the large scale. In this sense, Boltzmann is the fountain-head of modern physics.

Boltzmann in turn influenced Max Planck, who introduced the revolutionary idea of random behaviour into the field of energy at the end of the nineteenth century. When Einstein in two papers in 1905 demonstrated the random movements, first of atoms on the surface of a liquid, and then of units of light-energy as they strike a film of metal, the whole of modern physics on the minute scale lay in sight.

These advances on the continent of Europe were matched by similar interests in England. James Clerk Maxwell worked out the statistics of the behaviour of atoms in large numbers even before Boltzmann

Introduction

did. And the great school of mathematical statistics in England, whose pioneers were Francis Galton and Karl Pearson, took its impulse directly from the biological problems which Darwin raised.

One of the results of this fertilisation of physics by biology remains a major intellectual problem for both disciplines today. This is the problem of the different organisations of living and of dead nature. In some sense, which we can only vaguely grasp, the direction of evolution is towards more complex relations. Time on the scale of evolution has an arrow which, in some sense, points towards higher order. But in dead nature, the arrow of time points the other way. The atoms want always to move towards a state of lower order, towards an even mixture which will be undifferentiated and featureless. For dead nature, time is a running-down movement towards more probable, that is, more unordered states. By contrast, life is a constant resistance to this running-down of time, a constant choice, a constant re-creation of miraculously improbable states of order. This is the paradox which Darwin and Boltzmann made between them; and I look forward to the day when the social sciences will have equally heady speculations to share with biology and physics.

BASIL WILLEY

Darwin's Place in the History of Thought

WHAT IS THE HISTORY OF THOUGHT?

Not long ago I was privileged to exchange a few words, at a Cambridge party, with Darwin's distinguished grandson Sir Charles Darwin, and I mentioned that I had been invited to give this lecture on 'Darwin's Place in the History of Thought'. He twinkled at me, and said 'What *is* the history of thought?' What indeed! There are obviously many different kinds of thought, each with its own history; one can talk intelligibly of the history of thought about God, about the Universe, about man and his destiny, about the various branches of natural science, about the arts, about politics and society, about morality, education, and so forth. But the phrase 'history of thought', loosely though it is used in common parlance, has nevertheless some meaning; it means something wider, more inclusive, than the history of any one branch of speculation. Perhaps we may take it to mean the history of man's endless probings into the mystery of existence; his thoughts about the nature of reality, about the administration of the universe, its origin and destiny, his own place in it, and his relation to what can be known but not seen. It involves the history of scientific thought only in so far as science affects these ultimate matters, modifying our sense of the meaning of life. At any rate I hope I shall be excused for interpreting the phrase thus widely, for it is only by so doing that I can render even partially intelligible my presence as a speaker here today. Though an inveterate trespasser on other people's preserves, I have never yet had the effrontery to invade the field of biology or any of its specialised sub-divisions. Others will speak to you, with authority, on scientific and sociological themes; for my part I must be content to speak as an outsider, a person of merely literary training with an amateur interest in philosophical questions. As a teacher of English Literature at Cambridge I have long empha-

1

sized that what men think about the Universe they live in, about Nature and its laws, and about man's place in Nature, has a great deal to do with the literature in which they record and communicate their whole sense of life's quality and meaning. Students of literature, I believe, should therefore try to relate each period of literary history to the scientific theories which were then predominant. One reminds them, however, that it is not the actual theories which affect ordinary men and women; it is what the theories seem to mean in terms of their human hopes and fears. The scientist is actuated solely (or so we are told) by the desire for truth; his questions are 'What exactly is this thing?' 'What is it composed of?' 'How did it come about?' 'How does it work?' and the like. The ordinary human being, poet or peasant, asks 'How are we going to live in the light of this theory?' 'How does it affect our happiness, our prospects in this world and the next?' The answers to such questions are given partly by religion, partly by ethics and politics, but the feeling which lies behind the questions, the sense of what it means to be forced to ask them, is best conveyed by poets and men of letters in general. And the reactions of poets to scientific theories can usually be summarised in the exclamations 'How exhilarating!' 'How wonderful!'—or perhaps more often 'How depressing!' 'How appalling!' Darwin himself was not interested in the metaphysical or theological implications of his theory; his mind was not of the kind which tries to turn a scientific hypothesis into a complete philosophy of life. And yet, as I hope to illustrate, he was generally supposed, a century ago, to have revolutionised men's traditional ways of thinking about the universe, by banishing the notions of God and Final Cause, and substituting that of Blind Chance. To this subject I shall return later; but first let us take a brief glance at Darwin's place in the history of the evolutionary idea.

WHAT WAS DARWIN'S THEORY?

Samuel Butler used to complain that so many Darwinians spoke of Evolution as if it were Darwin's own invention, whereas Darwin's theory was merely that evolution had come about mainly by natural selection. By now it is generally realised, I suppose, that Darwin's importance lay not in promulgating Evolution itself, but in showing how it worked and making people believe in it. According to Butler, 'Buffon planted, Erasmus Darwin and Lamarck watered, but it was Mr Darwin who said "That fruit is ripe", and shook it into his lap'. This is misleading if it is taken, as Butler meant it to be taken, as an aspersion on Darwin's originality. Darwin did not arrive at his results by reading the works of his precursors, but by studying Nature herself with that infinite patience in observation, coupled with a certain visionary power, which together constitute what we call 'genius'. In fact, although Darwin had read his grandfather's *Zoonomia* in youth, he knew much less than many of his critics about the previous history of evolutionary thought, and was rather surprised when various 'anticipations' were pointed out to him. Butler, the *advocatus diaboli* in this case, was nearer the truth when he wrote (in *Life and Habit*, 1878):

> Less than twenty years age we never met with, or heard of, anyone who accepted evolution, . . . unless it was that someone now and again said that there was a very dreadful book going about like a rampant lion, called 'Vestiges of Creation' . . . Yet now, who seriously disputes the main principles of evolution ? . . . It is not he who first conceives an idea . . . but he who makes the people accept the main conclusion . . . who has done the greatest work as regards the promulgation of an opinion. And this is what Mr Darwin has done for evolution.[1]

Although I am sure that the present audience will not need to be reminded, I should like, before sketching the earlier history of 'the development idea', to remind myself of how Darwin, in the famous book whose centenary we are celebrating, summarised his own conclusions. Here are his words, which were inserted in the last chapter of the sixth edition of the *Origin of Species*:

> I have now recapitulated the facts and considerations which have thoroughly convinced me that species have been modified, during a long course of descent. This has been effected chiefly through the natural selection of numerous successive, slight, favourable variations; aided in an important manner by the inherited effects of the use and disuse of parts; and in an unimportant manner . . . by the direct action of external conditions, and by variations which seem to us in our ignorance to arise spontaneously.[2]

A simple-seeming statement: yet behind it stretch years of dogged and devoted labour, and beneath its every phrase lie the volcanic fires of controversy. 'That species have been modified'—but the immutability of species, and their origin in special acts of divine creation, was so generally held by theologians and naturalists alike before 1859, that Darwin, writing to J. D. Hooker in 1844 could say: 'At

3

Basil Willey

last gleams of light have come, and I am almost convinced (quite contrary to the opinion I started with) that species are not (it is like confessing a murder) immutable'. 'I think I have found out', he goes on, 'the simple way by which species become exquisitely adapted to various ends'.[3] All we need add, in order to complete this preliminary précis of Darwin's position, are the following points: the tendency of all offspring to vary, however slightly, from the parent stock; the enormous fecundity of living creatures, leading to the Malthusian struggle for existence, and the survival of the fittest. Nature, like man when breeding domesticated animals and plants, takes advantage of the favourable variations as and when they are thrown up, and suppresses the unfavourable. Creatures that happen to put forth variations advantageous to them in the struggle, survive and perpetuate themselves; the rest dwindle or perish. Since this Conference is concerned with Darwinism and the Study of Society, I ought also perhaps to mention at this point (what is familiar to you all) that it was the reading of Malthus on Population in 1839 which gave the final shake to the slowly-forming crystal of Darwin's theory. On his return from the voyage of 'The Beagle' (1831-6) he had begun systematically to arrange his observations and to collect every possible fact bearing upon the variation of creatures under domestication. He soon saw that 'selection was the keynote of man's success in making useful races of animals and plants', but how selection could operate in nature remained as yet a mystery to him. Then (as he says in the *Autobiography*):

> In October 1838 . . . I happened to read for amusement [an odd form of diversion, one might think] Malthus on *Population*, and being well prepared to appreciate the struggle for existence which everywhere goes on from long-continued observation of the habits of animals and plants, it at once struck me that under these circumstances favourable variations would tend to be preserved, and unfavourable ones to be destroyed. The result of this would be the formation of new species. Here then, I had at last got a theory by which to work. . . .[4]

In the Cambridge Centenary and Jubilee volume of 1909 (*Darwin and Modern Science*), J. Arthur Thomson pointed out that Malthus also furnished a clue to A. Russel Wallace, and that Herbert Spencer, before 1859, had published an article in the *Westminster Review* on the theory of population, in which he had 'come within an ace of recognising that the struggle for existence was a factor in organic evolution'. Thomson's comment is that Darwin, Wallace and Spencer

4

had all been 'led from a social problem to a biological theory', and that to grasp this correlation with contemporary social problems is more important than to ferret out hints and 'anticipations' from older books which Darwin had mostly not read. He further quotes an interesting passage from the article 'Biology' in *Chambers' Encyclopaedia*, in which the writer (P. Geddes) argues that the replacement of Paley by Darwin, as chief interpreter of the order of nature, is not just the replacement of anthropomorphism by science, but of an eighteenth century kind of anthropomorphism by a nineteenth century kind. For

'the place vacated by Paley's theological and metaphysical explanation', says Geddes, 'has simply been occupied by that suggested to Darwin and Wallace by Malthus in terms of the prevalent severity of industrial competition, and those phenomena of the struggle for existence which the light of contemporary economic theory has enabled us to discern, have thus come to be temporarily exalted into a complete explanation of organic progress.'[5]

This shows what happens when Darwin gets into the clutches of a smart intellectual. We are apt to surrender outright to such swift generalisations, yet how misleading is the suggestion that Darwin saw Nature in terms of the Industrial Revolution! Though a benevolent man, he never bothered about 'the condition of England question'; his thoughts hovered over the Galapagos Islands and the coast of Peru much more than over Manchester or Birmingham. On one point only his mind was fixed: how new species are formed; and Malthus meant nothing to him save for his fruitful hint on this process. As Thomson rightly adds, moreover, Darwin at once proceeded to *verify* the formula, and its validity does not depend on what suggested it. It can be safely said, on the other hand, that any debt of Darwin's to social theory was repaid with usury, for many sociologists and others afterwards tried to interpret human history on Darwinian lines, either approving or disapproving of competition and *laissez-faire* according to their political and economic views. Opinion was divided between those who thought that, to secure the best results, the struggle between individuals, classes and nations should go on; and those who held that man, whatever his ancestry, was now an ethical being, and must transcend and control the struggle in the interests of ideal ends.

Basil Willey

Now for our glance backwards—bearing always in mind that Darwin (like Wordsworth in this respect, if in no other) owed much more to Nature than to books. Darwin's 'general agent', 'bull-dog' and knight-at-arms, T. H. Huxley, in his chapter 'On the Reception of the "Origin of Species" ' (*Life and Letters of Charles Darwin*, Vol. II, Ch. V), after saluting Darwin as the Newton of biology, goes on to show that the influence of Darwinian ideas has spread far beyond that special field. 'The oldest of all philosophies', says Huxley with one of his fine rhetorical gestures—

> the oldest of all philosophies, that of Evolution, was bound hand and foot and cast into utter darkness during the millennium of theological scholasticism [Huxley's reading was far wider than Darwin's, but perhaps it did not include Augustine and Aquinas]. But Darwin poured new life-blood into the ancient frame; the bonds burst, and the revivified thought of ancient Greece has proved itself to be a more adequate expression of the universal order of things than any of the schemes which have been accepted by the credulity and welcomed by the superstition of seventy later generations of men.

The emergence of the philosophy of Evolution 'in the attitude of claimant to the throne of the world of thought', he adds, 'is the most portentous event of the nineteenth century'.[6] It is true enough that evolutionary ideas, of one sort or another, can be traced back to the pre-Socratic philosophers. It would be quite impossible in the space of one lecture (even if I were competent to do it) to tell the story in any completeness; most of you will know it already, and besides, the facts are set forth in H. F. Osborn's *From the Greeks to Darwin* (Columbia University Biological Series, No. 1, 1894). I will merely turn a spot-light upon a few points along the immense panorama.

Empedocles of Agrigentum (495-435 B.C.) taught that the world was composed of four elements continually tossed to and fro by the opposing forces of attraction (love) and repulsion (hate). From this chance play of love and hate Nature throws up all conceivable forms, including plants and animals. Many of these living forms are incomplete or monstrous, and only those are preserved which are fitted to survive.

On Aristotle (384-322 B.C.) we may dwell a little longer, for—as might be expected of so great a thinker—he touches upon all the relevant questions. It is especially interesting, too, that Aristotle is

6

the only ancient writer referred to by Darwin in the 'Historical Sketch' which he added to the third edition of the *Origin*, and that he seems to have misunderstood the drift of the passage he quotes from the *Physics*. Aristotle was a teleologist, seeing Nature as a graded system ordered towards the perfection of each form from the polyp up to man. Design and purpose are ever apparent in Nature; matter and force, regarded by the earlier philosophers as sole causes, are in truth (as Jaeger puts it) only 'nature's handymen; she herself is the builder proceeding according to an inner plan and idea'.[7] As a thinker who believed that Nature is purposive, striving always after the better, Aristotle makes a point of refuting Empedocles and others who had taught that chance ruled supreme, and that the existing forms and adaptations were simply those which survived because they happened to be thrown together *as if* by design. This is the passage referred to in Darwin's 'Historical Sketch', and I suspect that he only read that part of it which he quotes as having been pointed out to him by a friend. At any rate, he stands Aristotle on his head, praising him faintly for foreshadowing the principle of 'natural selection', and not noticing that the remarks he quotes are from the summary of the Empedoclean doctrine, which Aristotle gives merely to demonstrate its absurdity.[8]

I said a moment ago that I doubted whether Huxley had read Augustine or Aquinas, and my reason for this reference was that both the Father and the Schoolman can be said to have held views about the Creation far more consonant with Darwin's than is often supposed, and far more 'enlightened' than those of the fundamentalist Victorians attacked by Huxley. Augustine glossed the Creation story in Genesis by saying, in effect, that in the first days God created the plants and animals *causaliter*, that is to say, by infusing into the earth the necessary energy or potency so that it could thereafter produce the creatures by 'natural' unfolding, God resting from his labours. Aquinas, expounding Augustine, appears to sanction this view. Thus Pusey in 1878, while denouncing Darwin for his theory of man's descent, could yet admit Evolution in the animal and vegetable kingdoms as a theory in perfect accord with the teaching of western theology since Augustine, and not excluded by Scripture. Aubrey Moore, one of the Victorian theologians who, after the first furore about Darwinism had simmered down, did most to promote the peaceful co-existence of Science and Religion, argued that the anti-thesis between Creation and Evolution was unreal: 'The facts of Nature are the acts of God'. When we say 'God made us' we don't mean to deny the facts of reproduction; and similarly we may say 'God made the species' without denying his method of evolving them.

7

It was odd, Moore felt, that the question between the mutability or immutability of species should ever have appeared to be a religious question at all. Who invented the doctrine of immutability? not Augustine nor Aquinas nor Bacon; the true culprits were Milton, Ray and Linnaeus—and especially Milton, whose description of the creatures emerging fully-formed from the earth had been accepted as authoritative. Since we know that Milton was Darwin's favourite reading in his youth, and always accompanied him on his excursions from the 'Beagle', let us remind ourselves of the picture of creation given in *Paradise Lost*. It is that which Darwin spent the next twenty years in trying to blot out from his imagination:
[on the sixth day of creation God bids the earth bring forth beasts, each after his kind]

> The Earth obey'd, and straight
> Op'ning her fertile womb team'd at a birth
> Innumerous living creatures, perfect forms,
> Limb'd and full grown. . . .
> The grassy clods now calv'd; now half appear'd
> The tawny lion, pawing to get free
> His hinder parts, then springs as broke from bonds,
> And rampant shakes his brinded mane; the ounce,
> The libbard, and the tiger, as the mole
> Rising, the crumbl'd earth above them threw
> In hillocks; the swift stag from under ground
> Bore up his branching head; scarce from his mould
> Behemoth biggest born of earth upheav'd
> His vastness; fleec't the flocks and bleating rose
> As plants; ambiguous between sea and land
> The river horse and scaly crocodile.
> Book VII, 453 ff.

If then, neither the Bible, nor the Fathers, nor the Schoolmen support it, why should modern Christians feel obliged to defend an exploded scientific theory?[9]

DARWIN'S PLACE IN THE HISTORY OF EVOLUTIONARY THOUGHT

Evolutionary ideas were steadily gathering momentum from the Renaissance onwards, but the great period of the *praeparatio darwinica* was the eighteenth century, when the concepts of development, continuity, perfectibility, and descent from a common prototype, begin to appear piecemeal in the writings of philosophers and naturalists such as Leibnitz, Kant, Herder, Diderot, Bonnet (who invented the term 'Evolution'), Goethe, and above all in Buffon, Erasmus Darwin and Lamarck. The last three names bring us back to Darwin's 'Historical Sketch', which jumps in a few lines from

Aristotle to Buffon; but Darwin's treatment of them is perfunctory in the extreme, and it is reasonable to suppose that, apart from the above-mentioned reading of his grandfather's *Zoonomia* in early years, he was not deeply versed in them or conscious of any great debt to them. In his *Autobiography* he tells us that while a student at Edinburgh he had listened 'in silent astonishment' to a panegyric on Lamarck by Dr R. E. Grant, but 'without any effect on my mind'; and he adds that he had previously met with similar views in the *Zoonomia*, and that they too had produced no effect on him. He goes on at once to admit, however, that 'the hearing rather early in life such views maintained and praised may have favoured my upholding them under a different form in my *Origin of Species*'. As Lady Barlow says in her recent edition of the *Autobiography*, the important words here are 'in a different form';[10] Darwin felt that he had supplied the necessary foundation of fact for what had hitherto, to some extent, been airy speculation. Lamarck he consistently decried and probably undervalued; in one of his letters he calls Lamarck's work 'a wretched book' (which of Lamarck's books did he mean, and how much had he read of it?), and says (in another) that he got 'not a fact or idea from it'. Buffon he calls the first to approach descent with modification in a scientific spirit, but complains that Buffon's opinions 'fluctuated greatly at different periods', and that he did not examine the causes or means of transformation. We may perhaps say of Buffon, Erasmus Darwin and Lamarck that between them they had supplied nearly all the necessary ingredients, and that these ingredients, only needed the added tincture from Malthus, the idea of natural selection, and the massive substructure of Darwin's own observations, to produce the complete Darwinian dish. Buffon had taught the mutability of species under the direct influence of environment, the elimination of the unfit and the preservation of the fit through heredity. Erasmus Darwin traced back all life to a single 'filament' endowed with irritability and excitability, and shifted the emphasis from the Buffonian 'environment', to the Lamarckian effort on the part of creatures to attain needed structures: 'all animals', he said, 'undergo transformations which are in part produced by their own exertions in response to pleasures and pains, and many of these acquired forms or propensities are transmitted to their posterity'. Lamarck himself, who may or may not have borrowed from Erasmus Darwin, differed from Buffon and agreed with Erasmus in making environment act, not directly, but indirectly: thus, changed environment produces changed needs (*besoins*), these produce new habits, and new habits produce new or modified organs, which are passed on by heredity. Rudimentary organs are due to disuse. All three writers

9

replace supernatural creation by natural causation, and all presuppose a common origin for man and the apes—though Buffon, with an irony that escaped Darwin's notice but not Samuel Butler's, affected to recant this view and to submit to Revelation.

What, then, shall be said of Darwin's place in the history of evolutionary thought? To describe him as the heir of all the ages, the plucker of the ripe fruit, or even as the man who discovered how to fit together all the scattered hints thrown out by his predecessors, would be, for the reasons I have suggested, a misleading half-truth. Darwin arrived at his hypothesis, like a true scientist, through his own dealings with Nature, patiently pursued through more than twenty years, in the light of what was at first a wild surmise, but which was verified at every turn by the facts. Yet, looking back over the past history, we cannot help asking whether Darwin underestimated his debt to his many precursors. Did he even, possibly, play down their importance so as to exalt his own originality? The accusation by Samuel Butler, that Darwin had fraudulently claimed as his own what really belonged to others, can be dismissed at once as a malicious slander. No one who understands Darwin's nobility of character, his single-minded candour, and his over-sensitive care for truth, could entertain such a fantasy. It is enough to point to his magnanimous treatment of Wallace, and his ready acknowledgment of anticipations by others (such as Dr Wells and Patrick Matthew) when he afterwards came to hear of them. Yet, although he denied that the subject of evolution was in the air at the time, we are bound to believe that in some sense it *was* so; the seminal ideas were afloat, and were known to the instructed; and the grand conception of development by natural causation, which for three centuries had more and more been influencing every sphere of enquiry, and had recently achieved new triumphs in the nebular theory, in geology and in embryology—to say nothing of its effects on the interpretation of history, sacred and profane—all this had prepared a broad highway through which Darwin could pass like a conqueror.

DARWINISM AND RELIGION

I promised to return to the wider implications of our theme, so let me now say a few concluding words on Darwinism and traditional Christian thinking. Anyone acquainted with the hostile reviews, sermons and treatises evoked by the *Origin of Species* and *The Descent of Man*, will know that at that time Darwin was supposed by many to be a wicked infidel who had abolished God, undermined the authority of Scripture, degraded Man to the level of the beasts that perish, and

10

abandoned the universe to the control of Chance. Men had lived for so long with the idea of God as Creator, and of Nature as evidence of His purpose and design, that they were shocked to hear that creatures had 'just growed' instead of being made by the divine craftsman, and that the exquisite adaptations of organs to their environment were the result, not of design, but of the natural selection of variations that chanced to be favourable. Some there were who could accept all this for inorganic nature and the vegetable and animal kingdoms, but who shrank from the idea of man's pithecoid ancestry —a notion which Darwin had barely hinted at in the *Origin*, but which was seen to be implicit in his argument.

Darwin himself wondered what all the fuss was about, and regarded it with innocent surprise or mild irritation. 'With respect to the theological view of the question,' he wrote to Asa Gray (May 22, 1860), 'this is always painful to me. I am bewildered. I had no intention to write atheistically.' 'I do not attack Moses,' he said once to his friend the Vicar of Downe; 'and I think Moses can take care of himself.' In 1873, in answer to a Dutch correspondent, he wrote:

> . . . I may say that the impossibility of conceiving that this grand and wondrous universe, with our conscious selves, arose through chance, seems to me the chief argument for the existence of God; but whether this is an argument of real value, I have never been able to decide . . . Nor can I overlook the difficulty from the immense amount of suffering through the world. I am, also, induced to defer to a certain extent to the judgment of the many able men who have fully believed in God; but here again I see how poor an argument this is. *The safest conclusion seems to be that the whole subject is beyond the scope of man's intellect; but man can do his duty* (my italics).[11]

This is in close accord with the well-known utterance of a celebrated contemporary of Darwin's—also an Agnostic—George Eliot, on the theme of God, Immortality and Duty: 'how inconceivable the first, how unbelievable the second, and yet how peremptory and absolute the third'. In 1878, referring to an attack by Pusey, he wrote:

> Dr Pusey was mistaken in imagining I wrote the 'Origin' with any relation whatever to Theology . . . I may add that, many years ago, when I was collecting facts for the 'Origin', my belief in what is called a personal God was as firm as that of Dr Pusey himself, and as to the eternity of matter I have never troubled myself with such insoluble questions.[12]

11

Basil Willey

A year later (1878), he dictated the following reply to an earnest German student who had asked for a statement of his religious opinions:

Mr Darwin . . . considers that the theory of Evolution is quite compatible with the belief in a God; but that you must remember that different persons have different definitions of what they mean by God.

When the German student, unsatisfied with this meagre allowance, wrote back and asked for more, Darwin adopted the tactics which had served him so often and so well in evading unwanted committees, functions and invitations: he is old, he is out of health, he is preoccupied, and he cannot spare time to answer unanswerable questions. 'Science', he adds,

'has nothing to do with Christ, except in so far as the habit of scientific research makes a man cautious in admitting evidence. For myself, I do not believe that there ever has been any revelation. As for the future life, every man must judge for himself between conflicting vague probabilities.'[13]

In that same year (1879) he wrote to J. Fordyce: 'What my own views may be is a question of no consequence to anyone but myself'. This remark, so typical of Victorian individualism, is also very revealing of Darwin's mentality. He, the Newton of biology, the central and most influential figure in nineteenth century science, with a 'place in the history of thought'; he, the author of books which had convulsed the Church and shattered the simple faith of thousands, actually thought that he could keep his religious views to himself, that they had no bearing on his work, and that they mattered to nobody! The fact is, he figured in his own eyes as (what indeed in a sense he actually was) a country gentleman of ample means, retiring habits, bad health and, of course, a passion for natural history so obsessive that it crowded everything else out of his life. To a man so obsessed (*possessed* would be a better word) by his chosen pursuits, and so hampered by giddiness and other troublesome symptoms ('I *never* pass 24 hours without many hours of discomfort'), it seemed perverse and unkind of his critics and correspondents to insist upon cornering him with abtruse problems for which he had no time and no aptitude. In the same letter, he goes on:

But, as you ask, I may state that my judgment often fluctuates . . . In my most extreme fluctuations I have never been an Atheist

12

in the sense of denying the existence of a God. I think that generally (and more and more as I grow older), but not always, that
[*sic*] an Agnostic would be the more correct description of my
state of mind.[14]

We may remind ourselves that when Darwin went to Cambridge it
was with the idea of being ordained; that he there studied and admired
Paley, that when on board the 'Beagle' he was 'heartily laughed at by
several of the officers . . . for quoting the Bible as an unanswerable
authority on some point of morality', and that in later life he was
found, by some German phrenologists, to possess a 'bump of Rever-
ence developed enough for ten Priests'. So far was he from intending
any assault upon religion, that in the *Origin* itself he went out of his
way to disclaim the notion:

> I see no good reason why the views given in this volume should
> shock the religious feelings of anyone. It is satisfactory, as show-
> ing how transient such impressions are, to remember that the
> greatest discovery ever made by man, namely the law of the
> attraction of gravity, was also attacked by Leibnitz, as 'subversive
> of natural, and inferentially of revealed, religion'. 'A celebrated
> author and divine', he goes on (it was Charles Kingsley), 'has
> written to me that "he has gradually learnt to see that it is just as
> noble a conception of the Deity to believe that He created a few
> original forms capable of self-development into other and need-
> ful forms, as to believe that He required a fresh act of creation
> to supply the voids caused by the action of His laws".'

And he concludes the whole book with these words:

> There is grandeur in this view of life, with its several powers,
> having been originally breathed by the Creator into a few forms
> or into one; and that . . . from so simple a beginning endless
> forms most beautiful and most wonderful have been, and are
> being evolved.[15]

There might be grandeur in it for Kingsley, and Aubrey Moore,
and a few other stalwart liberals and modernists, but not for Samuel
Wilberforce or Dr Pusey or the general mass of believers and their
ecclesiastical spokesmen. For them, in spite of Darwin's pious
gesture of appeasement, it meant the banishment of the idea of God
the creator and designer to such a distance that it lost all religious
meaning. Darwin's vestigial theism was no comfort to them; he had

not attacked Moses, certainly; but if he were right, Moses must be wrong. It was the substitution of 'chance' for 'design' that caused most of the offence, and seemed to place Darwin in the atheistical succession from Epicurus and Lucretius and all the later materialists. It was of no avail for Darwin to explain, as he did, that in nature nothing happens by chance, but all according to the strict determination of physical law. 'Chance' does not mean 'no cause'; it means 'cause unknown'; it is, he said, a term which 'serves to acknowledge plainly our ignorance of the cause of each particular variation'. Yet he habitually spoke as if the useful variations, which Nature selects from the mass of useless ones, were (like the latter) thrown up at random; and if things happen like this, it was felt, they happen without the conscious purpose or design of an intelligent agent. Could an elaborate structure like the eye, for example, have been formed in this way? Darwin often admitted that he was 'staggered' (a favourite word of his) by the eye, and told Asa Gray (in 1860) that 'the eye to this day gives me a cold shudder'. Throughout his life Darwin had moods in which it seemed difficult or impossible to conceive 'this immense and wonderful universe, including man with his capacity of looking far backwards and forwards into futurity, as the result of blind chance or necessity'; [16] and at such times, as he says, 'I deserve to be called a Theist'. Yet, by his own admission also, these impressions gradually became weaker; disbelief 'crept over me at a very slow rate, but was at last complete. The rate was so slow that I felt no distress'. The Duke of Argyll records some significant words spoken to him by Darwin in the last year of the latter's life, during a talk about the wonderful contrivances in nature: 'I said it was impossible to look at these without seeing that they were the effect and expression of mind'. Darwin looked at him very hard, and said 'Well, that often comes over me with overwhelming force; but at other times', and he shook his head vaguely, adding, 'it seems to go away'.[17]

It went away, and with it went, as Darwin sorrowfully confessed in old age, his powers of responding to music, poetry and landscape, in all of which he had once delighted. 'My mind', he said, 'seems to have become a kind of machine for grinding general laws out of large collections of facts'. I quoted, a moment ago, Darwin's avowal that he was not an Atheist in the sense of denying the existence of God. But that subtle schoolman, Dr Pusey, said of him, as of modern scientists generally (as distinct from the older scientists from Copernicus to Newton and beyond), that he had done something worse than to deny God; he had *forgotten* Him. Worse, because denial at least implies the presence in the mind of the object denied, whereas it is of the essence of Darwinism to eliminate God, as far as may be,

14

from our thoughts about the creation and its history. Pusey connects this loss of spiritual perception—the common outcome of modern science—with the narrowing effects of specialisation, and quotes from Newman the observation that 'any one study . . . exclusively pursued, deadens in the mind the interest, nay the perception, of any other'.[18] And this is perhaps the heart of the religious criticism of all science, Darwinian or other, that in attending exclusively to the How it loses interest in the Whence and the Why. Science, *qua* science, must do this; its very *raison d'être* is to replace the supernatural by the natural, the unknown by the known, fable by fact, and while it is engaged upon this task it must be provisionally atheistic or cease to be itself. Perhaps Darwin would have been wiser not to mention the Creator at all in the *Origin*; as it was, he made people feel that he believed too much not to believe more, or too little not to believe less still. A God who breathed life into the primordial forms, and then rested from his work for ever after, did not satisfy the religiously-minded. Darwin had devoted himself so whole-heartedly to displacing divine acts and fiats by chance and selection, that he might as well have gone the whole way back to Epicurus and declared for the eternity of matter. But, as I have said, Darwin regarded all such questions as insoluble puzzles, and distractions from the real business of his life. It was very inconsiderate of 'clever' people to pester him with them, especially as he 'enjoyed' such poor health.

It would be absurd to blame Darwin for not having been a profound metaphysician or theologian; the work he did accomplish was more than enough for the lifetimes of several ordinary men. But there were and are others for whom God is no optional hypothesis, to be occasionally used when other explanations fail, but the central, all-demanding fact of experience; and it was left to such people to reconcile Darwinism with their faith if they could. The later history of Christian apologetics has shown that the thing could be done. It was done by declaring that God has not rested after the seventh day, but has been immanent in nature throughout, so that the facts of nature *are* the acts of God. One may go further and say that Darwin has positively helped to restore buoyancy to religion by forcing it to abandon some of its most untenable defences. Though scriptural fundamentalism was undermined by historical and textual criticism far more than by natural science, Darwin contributed his share to the weakening of that bibliolatry which was the bane of popular Protestantism. And in so far as he reduced the authority of the old argument from design, he was discrediting what had always been, in reality, a precarious line of defence. As Pascal had long ago said, Nature proves God only to those who already believe in Him on other

15

grounds. It is now possible for theologians to express surprise and regret that so much time was wasted in 'ridiculous debates as to whether the world was really created in six days, whether Adam and Eve actually existed, whether the serpent actually spoke', or whether the Flood really happened, and to take for granted that religion rests, not upon any assailable documents or outworn mythologies, but on the verifiable facts of spiritual experience. But, as Dr Vidler has said, 'many who now take advantage of this flexibility omit to acknowledge, or perhaps are unaware of, their debt to those who won it for them'.[19]

Darwin would turn in his grave if he could know that, at a centenary celebration of his *Origin of Species*, anyone would salute him as an unwitting champion of Christianity. But the subject proposed for this address was 'Darwin's Place in the History of Thought', and it seemed to me proper, in interpreting this widely, to refer not only to his place in the history of evolutionary theory, but also to some effects of his work, however unintended, in fields where though still an outsider I have for long been a half-tolerated trespasser.

REFERENCES

1. Samuel Butler, *Life and Habit*, 1924 ed., p. 276.
2. Darwin, *Origin of Species*, World's Classic edition, 1951, pp. 549-50.
3. Francis Darwin, *Life and Letters of Charles Darwin*, 1887, vol. II, p. 23.
4. Lady Nora Barlow (editor), *The Autobiography of C. Darwin*, London, 1958, p. 120.
5. J. Arthur Thompson, 'Darwin's Predecessors'; Ch. II in *Darwin and Modern Science*, Cambridge 1909, p. 15.
6. *Life and Letters of C. Darwin*, vol. II, p. 180.
7. Werner Jaeger, *Aristotle*, Oxford, 1934, p. 386.
8. cf. Aristotle's *Physics*, Book II, Ch. 8, trans. by W. D. Ross.
9. See Aubrey L. Moore, 'Darwinism and the Christian Faith', in *Science and the Faith*, 1887, especially pp. 178ff.
10. Lady Barlow, *op. cit.*, p. 152; see also p. 49.
11. *Life and Letters*, vol. I, pp. 306-7.
12. Ibid., vol. III, pp. 235-6.
13. Ibid., vol. I, p. 307.
14. Ibid., p. 304.
15. *Origin of Species*, ed. cit., pp. 550-1 and 560.
16. *Autobiography*, ed. cit., p. 92
17. *Life and Letters*, vol. I, p. 316 (footnote).
18. E. B. Pusey, *Un-Science, Not Science, Adverse to Faith*, 1878.
19. Alec R. Vidler, *Essays in Liberality*, 1957, pp. 63 and 17.

GEORGE SHEPPERSON

The Intellectual Background of Charles Darwin's Student Years at Edinburgh

FAMILY CONNECTIONS WITH EDINBURGH

The intellectual background of Charles Darwin's student years at Edinburgh should not be confined to the period from October 1825 to April 1827 when Darwin was a medical student. It is both wider and deeper: wider in the sense that family connections with the Edinburgh University *milieu* went back almost three-quarters of a century before Charles Darwin came to Edinburgh; deeper, in that it was never limited to official University figures and teachers but reached out into all levels of the society of what has often been termed the Scottish Golden Age, an exciting period when little Scotland made a large mark on a rapidly changing Europe and an emerging America, ideologically, scientifically, technically and politically.

The connections of the Darwin family with Edinburgh University were extensive and bring to mind relations with British universities of other famous families, such as the Bloomsbury set and Cambridge. When Charles Darwin, aged sixteen, and his brother Erasmus, aged twenty-one, went up to Edinburgh they represented the third generation of their family, on their mother's as well as their father's side, who had sought learning in or from the Athens of the North. Family ties meant much for Charles Darwin. It is not, therefore, artificial to trace his Edinburgh background to at least the 1750s and 60s, by which period his two notable grandfathers, the polymathic Erasmus Darwin and the potter Josiah Wedgwood had clearly established links with Edinburgh. Advanced thinkers, technicians of a very similar turn of mind and close personal friends,[1] the two were to become relatives in 1796 when Erasmus's second son married Josiah's eldest daughter. It is not unreasonable to suppose that, in such a close family circle, Charles Darwin, long before he went up to Edinburgh,

17

heard much of its intellectual eminence. This may, indeed, be one reason why he was so disappointed with the University when he became a student there.

Josiah Wedgwood, with an eye on business, may have consulted Joseph Black, the distinguished Edinburgh Professor of Chemistry, about 'minerals and fossils which might prove useful in his experiments for new porcellaneous bodies'.[2] Certainly, Black was on sufficiently good terms with Wedgwood to send him in 1786 a parcel of a piece of petrified wood from northern Ireland and some specimens of stone from Bengal. The parcel was entrusted to Josiah Wedgwood the younger, who had been sent to the Edinburgh Royal High School in 1782, and in 1786 was returning home after the first of three years as a medical student at Edinburgh University. With him, presumably, went his elder brother, John, who was at the Edinburgh medical school during 1785-6. In 1787 Thomas, younger brother of John and Josiah, arrived at Edinburgh for a two-year stay as a medical student. Thomas, eventually the most distinguished of them all, became the friend and benefactor of Coleridge. His 'Method of Copying Paintings upon Glass, and of making Profiles by the agency of Light upon the Nitrate of Silver' was presented to the Royal Institution in 1802 by Humphry Davy and gives him a leading place among the pioneers of photography. At Edinburgh, Thomas Wedgwood struck up a friendship with a fellow student, John Leslie,[3] the son of a Scottish carpenter, who subsequently became Professor of Mathematics at Edinburgh from 1805 to 1832 and wrote pioneering treatises on heat and light. At the invitation of the elder Wedgwood in 1790, Leslie visited the Wedgwood home, and acted as an informal tutor. He spent some time translating the French naturalist Buffon, and was given letters which opened to him the world of the new technocracy, personified by Wedgwood's and Erasmus Darwin's friends, James Watt and Matthew Boulton. In 1806, in his turn, Leslie received from the elder Wedgwood letters introducing his great-nephew who was also to study medicine in Edinburgh. This young relative, Henry Holland, later became a physician to Queen Victoria, and received a knighthood as an influential figure in the medical world of mid-nineteenth century Britain. It was to Holland's opinions on 'one primordial created form'[4] that Charles Darwin listened anxiously in the year of the publication of *The Origin of Species*.

The Edinburgh connections of Darwin's relations on his mother's side were thus fashioned well before his birth. The Darwin connection arose in 1754 when Erasmus Darwin, Charles's grandfather and predecessor in approach to the theory of evolution, came up to Edinburgh for the first of two years to continue medical studies begun at Cambridge. From this time until his death, Erasmus Darwin maintained close ties with Edinburgh and other Scottish intellectual circles, some members of which he drew into the activities of that group of pioneers of applied science, the Lunar Society. Particularly noticeable here are James Hutton,[5] the father of modern geology; Henry Moyes, the blind natural philosopher;[6] Hugh Blair, first holder of the Chair of Rhetoric at Edinburgh;[7] Sir John Sinclair,[8] pioneer agriculturalist and statistician; and, of course, James Watt[9]. The most important member, however, of Erasmus Darwin's Edinburgh circle was undoubtedly James Keir,[10] one of the first exponents of modern applied chemistry, whom Erasmus had known during his student years at Edinburgh, and with whom he was in constant touch. Erasmus Darwin's admiration for the solid virtues of Edinburgh learning may, indeed, have led him to suggest that Josiah Wedgwood should send his sons to Edinburgh.[11]

Hither, also, Erasmus Darwin sent three of his own sons. One was Charles Darwin's father, Robert Waring Darwin—not to be confused with Erasmus's brother of the same name, author of *Principia Botanica*.[12] A Fellow of the Royal Society, Robert Waring Darwin was, according to his son Charles, fond of theorising, and was 'incomparably the most acute observer'[13] Charles had ever known. Theorising and acute observation were characteristic of the learned world of Edinburgh during the years (1783-7) when Robert was a member of the University. Erasmus's sixth son, Francis Sacheverell, spent from 1804 to 1807 at Edinburgh, became a physician, and later lived for many years in a secluded part of Derbyshire, in a kind of naturalist's retreat, surrounded by animal oddities. 'Half-wild pigs ran about the woods and tamed snakes frequented the house.'[14]

But of all Erasmus's sons at Edinburgh the most distinguished was his eldest, Charles Darwin's namesake. This Charles Darwin was at the University from 1775 to 1778. He was awarded the Æsculapian Society's first gold medal for experimental work on pus and mucus,[15] and died in Edinburgh before he was twenty-one from the effects of a wound received while dissecting the brain of a child. He was buried in the family vault of Professor Andrew Duncan—the fearful dullness of whose lectures on Materia Medica at eight o'clock on a winter's morning[16] Charles Darwin the younger recalled with animus later in life. By all accounts, this elder Charles Darwin was a remarkable young man whose scientific zeal found in Edinburgh an ideal environment. If his nephew Charles in 1827 grew tired of the University, Charles Darwin the elder, half a century before, had asked to be taken away from Oxford, where he had spent a year, and to be sent to Edinburgh.

19

The Darwin-Wedgwood associations with Edinburgh did not finish with the younger Charles Darwin's forsaking its medical school for the clerical attractions of Cambridge, but it is not necessary here to trace their further ramifications during the nineteenth and twentieth centuries. The point has been made that the personal Edinburgh connection of the author of *The Origin of Species* may be said to range from his grandfather's first going to the University in 1754 to his own leaving it in 1828.

SCOTLAND'S GOLDEN AGE

Within these years is set what has often been called Scotland's and, in particular, Edinburgh's Golden or Augustan Age. There will, perhaps, always be argument about its chronological boundaries. One scholar has maintained that it formed an epoch from 1745 to 1832,[17] a period conveniently covering the life of Henry Mackenzie, author of *The Man of Feeling*, the Scottish best-seller of the 'natural' man. Another limits it to the half-century of Adam Smith's adult life, 1740-1790.[18] Certainly, in the first three decades of the nineteenth century much of the force of the so-called 'Scottish' or 'common sense' philosophy had been lost. Writing just after Darwin's Edinburgh period, Thomas Carlyle (who had lived in Edinburgh while Darwin was a student, although the two did not meet at this time) in his 1829 essay *Signs of the Times*[19] could notice the physical sciences engrossing 'more and more respect and attention' and could lament the death of the Scottish philosophy with its 'last amiable cultivator', Professor Dugald Stewart, of the chair of Moral Philosophy at Edinburgh from 1778 to 1810, who died in 1828. If such an approach would make the last three decades of the Scottish Golden Age a period of decline, there is also something to be said for beginning it earlier with Francis Hutcheson, Professor of Moral Philosophy at Glasgow from 1729 to 1746, who is most appropriately dubbed the father of the Scottish philosophy, and who spoke of man as 'the chief animal of the earth'.[20] Such an extension of the Golden Age would leave room for the Newcastle-upon-Tyne medical student at Edinburgh, Mark Akenside, who in 1741 published *The Pleasures of Imagination*, in which there are at least two passages which look forward to the 'notion of the gradualism of creation, development, evolution, call it what we will'[21] which runs throughout the productions of the period, its philosophy, its literature and its scientific treatises.

Yet it is, perhaps, more realistic to call the leading idea of the Caledonian Golden Age its belief in Nature. A recent German writer has spoken of 'the multiple awareness of nature' in Scottish literature from Gavin Douglas's sixteenth century translation of the *Aeneid*, 'that was to remain unrivalled until the eighteenth century'.[22] It was not an exclusively literary possession, this sharp, clear feeling for objective nature. It sprang from popular sentiment which kept it alive during the centuries. The supreme example of this sentiment is, of course, in Burns. In his poem 'To James Tennant of Glenconner', the poet commented on the popular character of the Scottish philosophy, using Adam Smith's *Theory of the Moral Sentiments* (1759) and Thomas Reid's *Inquiry into the Human Mind on the Principles of Common Sense* (1764) as his examples:

> I've sent you here by Johnie Simpson,
> Twa sage philosophers to glimpse on:
> Smith wi' his sympathetic feeling,
> An' Reid to common sense appealing.
> Philosophers have fought and wrangled,
> An' meikle Greek an' Latin mangled,
> Till, wi' their logic-jargon tir'd
> And in the depth of science mir'd,
> To common sense they now appeal—
> What wives and wabsters (weavers) see and feel!

Burns may have intended these remarks to be satirical but they do, in fact, illustrate very well the popular character of the Scottish attachment to nature: so that when in 1785 Burns claimed a common mortality with the mouse and apologised to it for breaking 'Nature's social union', he was not so much giving his own unique description of the old idea of the Great Chain of Being[23] as expressing the closeness of the common man in Scotland to Nature. Thus, in anticipation of a point which will arise later, one may say that Charles Darwin's instincts were sound when, during his Edinburgh student years, he made 'friends with some of the Newhaven fishermen, and sometimes accompanied them when they trawled for oysters, and thus got many specimens'.[24] Nor were his tastes at fault when he read before he came to Edinburgh *The Seasons* [25] by the Scottish-born poet, James Thomson. The sharpness of Thomson's observation of nature, and the fact that his approach to it was less anthropomorphic than Wordsworth's, have often been noticed.[26]

In the elaboration of the idea of Nature in the eighteenth century, as Professor Willey [27] has himself pointed out, David Hume played an important part. If Hume set Nature with Feeling rather than Reason—in which approach he was totally in accord with Scottish eighteenth-century philosophy—his speculations on Nature have their place in the development of evolutionary thought, and there is some evidence that the Darwins were not ignorant of them. Hume, for example, in his posthumous *Dialogues on Natural Religion* of 1779 speculated as follows:

> matter may be susceptible of many and great revolutions, through the endless periods of eternal duration. The incessant changes, to which every part of it is subject, seem to indicate some such general transformation.[28]

Elsewhere, he exclaimed:

> It is vain, therefore, to insist upon the uses of the parts in animals or vegetables and their curious adjustments to each other. I would fain know how an animal could subsist unless its parts were so adjusted? Do we not find that it perishes whenever this adjustment ceases, and that its matter corrupting tries some new form?[29]

If, in such passages, Hume comes close to the concept of Natural Selection, his work is not without a foretaste of the idea of the Struggle for Existence:

> ... why should man ... pretend to an exemption from the lot of the other animals? ... A perpetual war is kindled amongst all living creatures.[30]

Indeed, Erasmus Darwin, in his *Zoonomia*, which Charles Darwin read and admired before he came to Edinburgh, praised Hume's evolutionary approach and noted that in his posthumous works

> ... he concludes that the world itself might have been generated rather than created; that is, it might have been produced from very small beginnings, increasing from the activity of its inherent principles rather than by a sudden evolution of the whole by the Almighty fiat.[31]

In the section on generation from *Zoonomia*—the greater part of which, incidentally, was torn out of the Edinburgh University Library copy, presumably by some student who objected to the theological implications of its evolutionary ideas—in which these words occur, Erasmus Darwin contrasted the mechanical approach to nature with the evolutionary. From this point of view, it is interesting to note that during his second year at Edinburgh, 1755-6, William Cullen became joint Professor of Chemistry. It was Cullen and other physicians who were at this time beginning to throw off what Erasmus Darwin's chemist friend from Edinburgh, James Keir, called 'the Boerhaavian yoke'.[32] This reference was to the great Leyden teacher of medicine, Hermann Boerhaave, whose mechanical tendencies had been

22

constructive and fruitful in the early eighteenth century. On those tendencies had been raised some of the initial greatness of the Edinburgh medical school, but towards its end they were proving constrictive. Keir in a letter to Charles Darwin's father in 1802 made clear the distinction between the mechanical character of Boerhaave's approach to man and Erasmus Darwin's evolutionary attitude, when he referred to

> the narrow Boerhaavian system, in which man was considered as an hydraulic machine whose pipes were filled with fluid susceptible of chemical fermentations, while the pipes themselves were liable to stoppages and obstructions (to which obstructions and fermentations all diseases were imputed) [as contrasted with] the more enlarged consideration of man as a *living being* . . .[33]

By the time of Hume's posthumous writings, however, this mechanical mode of thought was becoming less and less representative of the Edinburgh intellectual scene. Evolutionary concepts, albeit often of a rudimentary kind, had already crept into many fields of Scottish learning. It should be unnecessary to detail them here, because they have been investigated with some thoroughness by several writers in the last three decades, and there are signs that the mid-eighteenth to early nineteenth century Scottish school of thinkers has not yet lost its attractions for historians and students of the social sciences.

The Scottish school's search for origins and its use of the comparative method are indicated by some of the titles of representative works: John Millar's *Origin of the Distinction of Ranks* (1771); Lord Monboddo's *On the Origin and Progress of Language* (1773-92); John Gregory's *Comparative View of the State and Faculties of Man with those of the Animal World* (1764). This emphasis on origins and comparisons is open to the same kind of criticism as that which modern social anthropologists, particularly the severer functionalists, have levelled at history. Furthermore, the fascination of all manifestations of primitive society for Scottish intellectuals of the period can produce the same kind of objections as the hypothetical Marxist category, primitive communism, has so often provoked from sociologists. And much of the evolutionism of the Scottish school was close to the Great Chain of Being concept. A good example of this is provided by *The Philosophy of Natural History*, an influential work, a copy of which was in Charles Darwin's library, published in 1790 by William Smellie, naturalist, antiquarian, friend of Monboddo, printer to Edinburgh University and editor of the first three volumes of the *Encyclopaedia Britannica*.[34] In Smellie's words:[35]

23

There is a graduated chain of existence [in which] every creature is perfect, according to its destination.

And yet Smellie could come close to the Darwinian idea of evolution when he wrote that:

Man, in his lowest condition, is evidently linked both in the form of his body and the capacity of his mind, to the large and small orang-outang.

Mention of the beloved orang-outang of the eighteenth century serves to introduce the most notable figure of the Scottish Golden Age, a man for whom a prime place in the history of evolutionary thought has been claimed: James Burnet, Lord Monboddo. Although Charles Darwin seems to have referred directly to Monboddo perhaps only in *The Descent of Man*,[36] it is likely that he was acquainted with his ideas, if only at second hand, before he left Edinburgh. Even if he did not hear of them from his grandfather, Erasmus, he borrowed the whole of Boswell's *Johnson* from the University Library during his first year as a student at Edinburgh[37] and he may have learned something about Monboddo from these volumes which afford evidence of the acrimonious controversy between Samuel Johnson and the Scottish judge.[38] The distinguished American historian of ideas, Arthur O. Lovejoy, has written enthusiastically of Monboddo's 'hypothesis of the common descent of all anthropoids, [which] suggested by implication a general law of organic evolution'; and has remarked that 'It is not surprising, therefore, that a countryman of his has claimed for him—and therefore for Scotland—the credit usually given to the author of *The Origin of Species*.'[39] But enthusiasm for Monboddo's undoubted place in the great chain of ideas which leads to *The Origin of Species* can be taken too far and it seems more reasonable to suppose, with Miss Gladys Bryson, that Monboddo was 'no precursor of Charles Darwin since he was not concerned with the origin of new species. Species were as fixed for Monboddo as for Linnaeus or any other believer in the Scale of Nature'[40]—nor, indeed, is there much in common between Monboddo's and Darwin's ideas on the origins of language.[41]

The Edinburgh man of these times who is closest to Charles Darwin's thought is most probably James Hutton, who between 1783 and 1795 produced his evolutionary *Theory of the Earth*, the forerunner of modern geology. There were family links with Hutton, who knew and corresponded with Erasmus Darwin[42] and seems to have had some contacts with the Wedgwoods.[43] But the real links between

24

Hutton and Charles Darwin are to be sought in the similarity of their methods of thinking. Not only did Hutton approach Darwin through his influence on Lyell but, as a practical Berwickshire farmer in the vanguard of the Agricultural Revolution in Scotland, came close to Darwin's thought on animal breeding. As Sir Edward B. Bailey has pointed out, Hutton's work in manuscript entitled *Principles of Agriculture* resembles closely in some places Darwin's ideas on variation and natural selection.[44] In some ways, Hutton is the outstanding representative of the Scottish Golden Age. Beginning as a law and medical student at Edinburgh, at a time when these faculties were gaining international fame, he went on to become not only the father of modern geology and the forerunner of many modern agricultural techniques but also wrote an epistemological work and went into partnership for the manufacture of sal ammoniac, in this way becoming a pioneer of what the Clows have called the 'Chemical Revolution'. Some of his theories, indeed, were confirmed in the Leith glass works of his friend, Sir James Hall.[45] Hutton, a man of many talents like his friend, Erasmus Darwin, thus spans the philosophical, scientific and industrial aspects of Scotland's Golden Age. His theories were attacked for their atheistic implications as Darwin's were a half-century later. Hutton was both a pure and an applied scientist, an amateur and a professional, and his work has that distinct combination of theory and practice, with its understanding of the importance of both detail and design, which characterizes much of the work of Charles Darwin.

DARWIN AT EDINBURGH

These parallels are worth bearing in mind when one approaches Charles Darwin's actual student period at Edinburgh. In his autobiography, Darwin left a famous criticism of these years.[46] As far as academic studies were concerned, he believed that he had wasted his time at Edinburgh. He was sickened with its lectures; he saw no advantages and many disadvantages in them, compared with reading. Later, he told his half-cousin, Francis Galton, that all that he had learned of value had been self-taught[47]—though Galton in his 1874 *English Men of Science*, in which he made use of Darwin's testimony, praised the Scottish universities' lecturing system.[48]

Darwin's strictures on the Edinburgh system have been received by some almost as a complete condemnation of his Edinburgh period. To see this in perspective, therefore, it is necessary to remember that he referred mainly to formal 'academic studies'. It is also worth noting the carefully considered statement about the teaching at

Edinburgh University by Professor L. J. Saunders in his *Scottish Democracy, 1815-1840*:[49]

> The science classes began to move away from formal exposition, and if the young Darwin was disappointed with the instruction at Edinburgh, others, expecting less, remarked on the increasing use of laboratory, museum and field excursion. But one of the most important educational agencies developed outside the class altogether. In contrast to the conventional bias of the English universities, and to the politically controlled European schools, the Scottish students were left free to associate and discuss at their pleasure. In the numerous student societies which met in the university buildings and in which a member of the university faculty appeared only as an invited guest, there was something more than a practice of good fellowship. The young lawyers, doctors and divines met for debate; wits were sharpened on contemporary issues; a less rhetorical style was formed and was expected to support its display of dialectic by an appeal to evidence; and those Englishmen who came north during the war years learned to appreciate and long remembered, amid all the Doric uncouthness, the surprising and sometimes brilliant commerce of ideas in the university societies.[50]

When it is remembered that Darwin was a member of the Edinburgh students' Plinian Society and that he attended meetings of the Wernerian Natural History Society, the Royal Medical Society, and the Royal Society of Edinburgh while he was at the University, these words have an additional significance.

Among those students who expected less than Darwin from Edinburgh, and therefore saw more in its curricula, were Thomas Carlyle[51] and Samuel Smiles. When he was a student at Edinburgh in 1812, Carlyle, like Darwin fourteen years later, took the natural history course of Professor Robert Jameson, the opponent of the Huttonian theories of geology. To Darwin, Jameson was 'incredibly dull'[52] and he claimed that he filled him with a distaste for geology—though Darwin had to admit that Jameson played an important part in the founding of the Edinburgh University students' Plinian Society, which gave him the opportunity of reading his first scientific paper.[53] Carlyle, on the other hand, noted how Jameson would 'run off the rails', 'quote Dante and other fellows',[54] and then return in a half-humorous manner to his subject. Carlyle bore witness to the vitality of the student societies at Edinburgh, and his comments suggest that Darwin may have taken more from them than he realised:

What they call evolution is no new doctrine [said Carlyle]. I can remember when Erasmus Darwin's *Zoonomia* was still supplying subjects for discussion and there was a debate among the students whether man was descended from an oyster or a cabbage.[55]

A similar tribute to the evolutionary doctrines in the air at Edinburgh was made by Samuel Smiles, who went there from Haddington in 1830 to study medicine. When Darwin's matured views on evolution were published, Smiles, writing in his autobiography, noted their similarities to the teachings of 'Dr Fletcher',[56] a lecturer in the University's extra-mural school of medicine, whose course he had taken:

I felt that Fletcher, an extensive reader . . . [who] brought all the sciences of Europe to bear upon his subject had long before expounded very much the same views or at all events had heralded his [Darwin's] approach.[57]

And, of course, it is also worth remembering that Jameson's lectures concluded with some account of the philosophy of zoology, in which the first subject was entitled 'The Origin of the Species of Animals'.[58]

It is, therefore, evident that Darwin's remarks on his Edinburgh years are likely to be misleading. This was noticed not long after they were first published in 1887 in Francis Darwin's edition of his father's life and letters. An anonymous writer contributed two articles in defence of the Edinburgh system to *The St James's Gazette* for 16 and 17 February, 1888.[59] His articles are important historical evidence today, because he had access to the University Library's record-book of borrowings for the years 1825-27 which has since been lost. From this, it appears that Charles Darwin and his brother, Erasmus, took out more books from the Library than any other students in the academic year 1825-26, and that Darwin read thoroughly in medical subjects. Furthermore, this anonymous author—who evidently knew the Edinburgh scene well—criticizes Darwin's statement that he 'was not urged' to practise dissection, saying that, if Darwin could not bear the subject at the hands of Monro, he could have gone to Knox, of Burke and Hare fame, whose classes attracted many students. This anonymous defence of the Edinburgh system deserves more attention than it has yet received.

Four years later, speaking on Scottish zoology at the first meeting of the Edinburgh University Darwinian Society, J. Cossar Ewart, Edinburgh Professor of Natural History, gave a valuable survey of natural history in Scotland, estimated Darwin's experiences at Edinburgh (particularly with the Plinian Society) and concluded that these years were 'an excellent preparation for his great life work'.[60] Especially interesting is Ewart's account of Dr Robert Grant,[61] an Edinburgh medical graduate and an extra-mural lecturer of the University with whom Darwin struck up a friendship in 1825-27. Ewart's tribute to Grant, an admirer of Lamarck and his evolutionary doctrines who became Professor of Comparative Anatomy and Zoology at London from 1827 to 1874, suggests that Darwin's picture in his autobiography of Grant's influence on him is, if anything, an understatement.

Defences of Edinburgh in Darwin's day have followed from time to time.[62] The most important is undoubtedly the 1935 paper to the Royal Society of Edinburgh by Professor J. H. Ashworth.[63] This scholarly account made use of a naturalist's notebook which Darwin began at Edinburgh, and provides a clear picture of the development of his zoological thinking at the University. Surprisingly, however, Professor Ashworth did not use the 1888 *St. James's Gazette* articles, and he failed to collect the minor but interesting testimony in 1882 by W. F. Ainsworth, surgeon, geologist and traveller, a former student at Edinburgh with Darwin, who noted that they went on many private expeditions on the east coast of Scotland, on one of which they were benighted at 'Inch Keith but found refuge in the lighthouse'.[64] Professor Ashworth reaches the conclusion that, from the evidence in the notebook he began during his last five and a half weeks at Edinburgh 'Darwin had acquired the methods of collecting and of identification of specimens and the faculty of careful observation and interpretation which he applied and developed with such remarkable success when the great opportunity came to him'.[65] Because of this, it is surprising that Professor Ashworth's paper was not noted with the scanty evidence of his years at Edinburgh which is given in the unexpurgated version of Darwin's autobiography that was published in 1958.[66]

Two decades later, Professor James Ritchie, speaking at the Robert Jameson centenary commemoration of the Royal Society of Edinburgh,[67] brought forward further material for the defence of the Edinburgh system in Darwin's student years. Impressive here was his account of Jameson's work in building up the University Museum, almost from scratch. At his death in 1852, it had 74,453 specimens from all parts of the world.[68] When Darwin noted the Museum in his autobiography he did not speak of Jameson's part in its growth or note that its Assistant-Keeper, William MacGillivray, later Professor of Natural History at Aberdeen, who took a friendly interest in the young Darwin and gave him 'some rare shells',[69] was Assistant and Secretary to Jameson.[70]

DARWIN AND THE SCOTTISH PHILOSOPHY

Such accounts, with the additional evidence from Darwin's wider Edinburgh background, indicate that, if the voyage of the *Beagle* from 1831-36 and his encounter with Malthus's *Essays on the Principle of Population* in 1838 are the more immediate grounds in which the beginnings of *The Origin of Species* may be sought, yet the streams of Scottish thought, and the careful and observant manner in which Scottish scientists and technicians of the Golden Age combined theory and practice, had no small part to play in bringing the young Darwin to these grounds. That there is so little direct evidence for an adequate documentation of Edinburgh and Scottish influences on the young Darwin—only two letters, for example, appear to have survived from his Edinburgh student days[71]—makes the problem both fascinating and frustrating for the historian of ideas. Darwin's writings afford only a very limited assistance—a fact which is perhaps explained by Professor Jacques Barzun's remark that 'Darwin was not at home with ideas'.[72] Although this is a sweeping generalization, it does reflect Darwin's preoccupation with the detailed evidence for substantiating his theories rather than with the processes of thought which had launched these theories into the world.

Darwin's ideas clearly belong to the same environment as the Scottish philosophy—which is not surprising if one remembers the 'important fact about the Scottish philosophers that is generally ignored is that they were the dominant philosophical school in Great Britain for just about a hundred years'.[73] How such ideas and methods reached Darwin is a matter for speculation. There is no evidence from the catalogue of his library that he read directly any of the Scottish philosophers,[74] though he did possess works by writers such as William Smellie who had been influenced by them. Some of their ideas, refracted through the new technological world which the Scottish Industrial Revolution did so much to create, may have reached him from his Wedgwood and Darwin relations, who were in close touch with the new technology. Perhaps he drew upon the resources of the Scottish philosophy from its contributions to the general contemporary climate of opinion, in such a way that the links between this philosophy and his own ideas form a problem of relationships similar to that between the sociological thought of John Millar and Karl Marx. Marx may not have read a word of Millar, whose sociology is similar in many ways to Marx's own.[75] Some elements, indeed, of the Scottish philosophy may have been acquired by Darwin after he left Edinburgh. This is suggested by the reference in *The Origin of Species*[76] to the thought of Edward Forbes, Jameson's successor in 1855 to the

Edinburgh Chair of Natural History. When Darwin referred to Forbes's insistence that 'there is a striking parallelism in the laws of life throughout time and space; the laws governing the succession of forms in past times being nearly the same with those governing at the present time the differences in different areas' he is echoing the spirit of the uniformitarianism of the Scottish school, which Forbes, a medical student at Edinburgh shortly after Darwin, must have appreciated.

From the Scottish 'commonsense' philosophy of the eighteenth century two tendencies emerged. First, its 'realistic intuitionism' rapidly paved the way for 'objective idealism'.[77] Even Thomas Brown, Professor of Moral Philosophy at Edinburgh from 1810-1820 —whose system, with that of Erasmus Darwin, has been claimed as a foundation for 'scientific work in physiological psychology and biology',[78] and who is said to have revolted against the authority of the 'commonsense' philosophy, although he was a pupil of Dugald Stewart[79]—made his academic reputation with a criticism in 1798 of *Zoonomia*, in which many of his objections[80] to Erasmus Darwin's evolutionary theories anticipate the opposition to *The Origin of Species*. From this tendency of the Scottish philosophy, Charles Darwin, ultimately, would have profited little.

With the other tendency of the Scottish philosophy, however, Darwin had much in common: the meticulous search for detail in support of one's hypotheses. In history, this produced that typical Scottish amateur of learning, the antiquarian.[81] In the sciences, its representatives were the collectors of data of all kinds, from the writers of the first *Statistical Account of Scotland* (1791-1799) to the geologists and naturalists, many of them amateurs and poor men. Many were the 'scholar gypsies' in Scotland's Golden Age. One would give much to know more about that 'very pleasant and intelligent man'[82] to whom Darwin paid tribute in his autobiography, the Edinburgh Negro taxidermist, who had travelled with the eccentric naturalist, Charles Waterton. Whether with his friends, the Newhaven fishermen, or with Waterton's Negro or with fellow students (some of whom subsequently had distinguished careers[83]), on private expeditions, Darwin could easily have encountered many of these talented Scottish amateurs of science. Such a person was John Scott, 'no common man' to Darwin,[84] with whom he was in touch in the 1860s, and who worked as a gardener at the Edinburgh Botanical Gardens, presumably 'in order to gratify his passion for natural history'. The Scottish nineteenth century is full of such men: a fact which demonstrates once again that the intellectual background to Darwin's student years at Edinburgh is not to be sought exclusively within the walls of the University. Alexander Wilson, the Paisley weaver, who wrote the first work on American ornithology, which Jameson edited for British publication[85]; George Miller of Dunbar, pioneer of popular scientific journalism, with his *Book of Nature Laid Open*[86]; Hugh Miller of Cromarty of *Old Red Sandstone* fame; David Livingstone[87] of Blantyre, whose contributions to other fields of learning besides geography are slowly being realised; Thomas Edward, cobbler naturalist of Banff, whose life was written by Samuel Smiles, are but a few examples. With this tradition in mind, it can be appreciated that it was not accidental that Patrick Matthew[88], Scottish Chartist author of the 1831 *Naval Timber and Arboriculture* with its anticipation of Natural Selection, in Darwin's worlds 'clearly saw the full force of the principle of natural selection'; or that an Edinburgh publisher of humble origins, Robert Chambers, in 1844 published *The Vestiges of the History of Natural Creation*. Both of them were noted in the historical sketch of evolutionary ideas which Darwin added to the third edition of *The Origin*.

In this sketch, Darwin mentioned Robert Grant and his own grandfather, Erasmus, in addition to Matthew and Chambers; these four figures bear testimony to the Scottish link with Darwin. If Erasmus Darwin was given what has sometimes appeared to be only a grudging footnote, eighteen years later this was to some extent put right in Charles Darwin's biographical introduction to Ernst Krause's study of his grandfather. There is enough material in this introduction to confirm the impression of the strength of the Darwin connection with Edinburgh.

And in this introduction Darwin quotes from his grandfather concerning his uncle Charles, who had 'sighed to be removed to the robuster exercise of the medical school of Edinburgh'.[89] If Charles Darwin the younger sighed to be removed *from* this robuster exercise of the Edinburgh medical school, that school and its environment had certainly left their mark on two previous generations of those stars of the rising British scientific and technical middle classes, the Wedgwood and Darwin families, membership of which, in their particular setting and at their particular time, almost persuades one that there is such a thing as inevitability in history—and that if any man was destined to write *The Origin of Species* it could have been no other than Charles Darwin.[90]

REFERENCES

1. Eliza Meteyard, *The Life of Josiah Wedgwood*, London, 1865, I, pp. 404-411; Ernst Krause, *Erasmus Darwin*, London, 1879, pp. 29-33; Archibald

George Shepperson

and Nan L. Clow, *The Chemical Revolution*, London, 1952, 96, 612. Cf. Henrietta Lichfield, ed., *Emma Darwin, A Century of Family Letters*, London, 1915, passim.

2. Eliza Meteyard, *A Group of Englishmen*, London, 1871, p. 36; and for the rest of this paragraph, pp. 26-7, 34-8, 148-66, 203, 309-10. See also Clow, op. cit., p. 312.

3. In addition to the above, see David Alec Wilson, *Carlyle Till Marriage*, London, 1923, pp. 83-5; and *D.N.B.*

4. Francis Darwin, ed., *Life and Letters of Charles Darwin*, London, 1887, II, p. 251.

5. Hesketh Pearson, *Doctor Darwin*, London, 1930, p. 161.

6. Ibid., p. 232.

7. Ibid., p. 232.

8. Clow, op. cit., p. 490; see also Krause, op. cit., pp. 112-3.

9. Ibid., passim.

10. Krause, op cit., pp. 13-14, 49-50; Clow, op. cit., 95-109, 133, 203, 496, 587, 593, 612.

11. Meteyard, op. cit., p. 34.

12. Meteyard, op. cit., p. 254, footnote 2 is obviously mistaken: cf. Francis Darwin, op. cit., I, p. 4.

13. Krause, op. cit., p. 85.

14. Francis Galton, *English Men of Science*, London, 1874, p.47.

15. Charles Darwin, *Experiments establishing a criterion between mucaginous and purulent matter*, Lichfield, 1780; Krause, op. cit., pp. 80-3.

16. Francis Darwin, op. cit., I, p. 36.

17. Harold William Thompson, *A Scottish Man of Feeling*, London, 1931, pp. 1, 440-4, etc. Cf. also Michael Joyce, *Edinburgh, The Golden Age, 1769-1832*, London, 1951, p. 2.

18. C. R. Fay, *Adam Smith and the Scotland of his Day*, Cambridge, 1956, p. 2.

19. *Edinburgh Review*, XLIX, 1829, pp. 444-5; Henry Laurie, *Scottish Philosophy in its National Setting*, Glasgow, 1902, p. 249.

20. Gladys Bryson, *Man and Society. The Scottish Inquiry of the Eighteenth Century*, Princeton, 1945, p. 56.

21. S. I. Tomkieff, 'James Hutton and the Philosophy of Geology', *Proceedings of the Royal Society of Edinburgh*, Section B (Biology), LXIII, 1950, p. 399.

22. Kurt Wittig, *The Scottish Tradition in Literature*, Edinburgh, 1958, p. 86; see also pp. 85-90, 123-5, 192-4, etc.

23. Arthur O. Lovejoy, *The Great Chain of Being*, Cambridge, Mass., 1942.

24. Francis Darwin, op. cit., I, p. 39.

25. Ibid., p. 33.

26. Cf. Basil Willey, *The Eighteenth Century Background*, London, 1940, p. 210; Wittig, op. cit., pp. 154-5; Lovejoy, op. cit., p. 240.

27. Op. cit., p. 111.

28. Ed. T. H. Green and T. H. Grose, *The Philosophical Works of David Hume*, London, 1878, II, p. 419.

29. Ibid., p. 428.

30. Ibid., p. 436.

31. Erasmus Darwin, *Zoonomia*, London, 1794, I, p. 509.

32. Krause, op. cit., p. 13.

33. Ibid., p. 13.

34. John Kay, *A Series of Original Portraits*, Edinburgh, 1877, I, p. 207.

32

35. Quoted in Bryson, op. cit., p. 62.
36. London, 1885, p. 572.
37. *St. James's Gazette*, XVI, 2403, 16 February 1888, p. 5.
38. Ed. George Birkbeck Hill and L. F. Powell, *Boswell's Life of Johnson*, Oxford, 1934-1950, six vols., see index, Vol. VI, p. 278, 'Monboddo'.
39. Arthur O. Lovejoy, *Essays in the History of Ideas*, Baltimore, 1948, p. 61.
40. Bryson, op. cit., pp. 76-7.
41. Cf. Bryson, op. cit., pp. 236-7; also the criticisms of Darwin's linguistic theories in Richard Albert Wilson, *The Miraculous Birth of Language*, London, 1941, pp. 70-84.
42. E.g. Krause, op. cit., pp. 33-4.
43. Clow, op. cit., p. 312.
44. Sir Edward B. Bailey, 'James Hutton, Founder of Modern Geology,' *Proceedings of the Royal Society of Edinburgh*, Section B (Biology), LXIII, 1948-9, Part IV, pp. 361-2; see also pp. 351-400 for excellent material on Hutton.
45. S. F. Mason, *A History of the Sciences*, London, 1953, p. 326.
46. Francis Darwin, op. cit., I, pp. 36-42, 46, 48.
47. Ibid., III, p. 177.
48. Galton, op. cit., pp. 225-6; see also pp. 215-6, 242 and 255.
49. Edinburgh, 1950, p. 310.
50. Cf. Galton, op. cit., p. 242.
51. But cf. Joyce, op. cit., p. 100.
52. Nora Barlow, ed., *The Autobiography of Charles Darwin*, London, 1958, p. 52: this restores the omitted name in Francis Darwin, op. cit., I, pp. 41 and 42. It is also noteworthy that Francis Darwin, ibid., p. 36 left out the name of Monro (restored but misspelt by Barlow, ibid., p.47). Why Francis Darwin spared the feelings of Jameson and Monro by leaving out their names from his father's autobiography and yet included (p. 36) the name of Andrew Duncan (against whom a similar charge of dullness in his lectures was made), a friend of the family (see Krause, op. cit., p. 82; Charles Darwin, *Experiments*, op. cit., pp. iii-iv) is something of a mystery. For defences of the three men see J. H. Ashworth, 'Charles Darwin as a Student in Edinburgh, 1825-1827', *Proceedings of the Royal Society of Edinburgh*, Session 1934-5, LV, Part II, 10, pp. 97-101. But cf. *Edinburgh Evening Dispatch*, 22 May 1888, p. 2 for an attack on Duncan's lecturing methods.
53. Francis Darwin, op. cit., p. 39; J. Cossar Ewart, *Address on Scottish Geology delivered at the first meeting (17th November 1891) of the University Darwinian Society*, Edinburgh, 1892, pp. 18-19; Ashworth, op. cit., pp. 102-6.
54. Wilson, op. cit., p. 87.
55. Ibid,. p. 73.
56. John D. Comrie, *History of Scottish Medicine*, London, 1932, II, pp. 630-1.
57. *The Autobiography of Samuel Smiles*, London, 1905, ed. Thomas Mackay, p. 35.
58. Sir Alexander Grant, *The Story of the University of Edinburgh*, London, 1884, II, p. 433.
59. XVI, 2403, p. 5, 2404, p. 7.
60. J. Cossar Ewart, op. cit., p. 20.
61. Ibid., pp. 12-19.
62. E.g. Professor J. Arthur Thomson in *Famous Edinburgh Students*, Edinburgh, 1914, pp. 146-8.

63. Ashworth, op. cit., pp. 97-113.
64. *The Athenaeum*, 2846, 13 May, 1882, p. 604. Cf. also remarks on Ainsworth, Darwin and the Plinian Society in *Edinburgh Evening Dispatch*, 22 May 1888, p. 2.
65. Ashworth, op. cit., p. 112.
66. Barlow, op. cit., p. 46, footnote 1.
67 James Ritchie, 'A Double Centenary—Two Notable Naturalists, Robert Jameson and Edward Forbes', *Proceedings of the Royal Society of Edinburgh*, Section B. (Biology) LXVI, Part I (No. 3), 1955-6, pp. 29-58.
68 Ibid., pp. 39-40.
69. Francis Darwin, ed., *Life*, op. cit., I, p. 42.
70. Ashworth, op. cit., p. 110.
71. Francis Darwin and A. C. Seward, ed., *More Letters of Charles Darwin*, London, 1903, I, pp. 5-8. See also *Edinburgh Evening Dispatch* (mistakenly called *Weekly Dispatch* in Barlow, op. cit., p. 46), 22 May 1888, p. 2, columns 5-7, for an article on Darwin at Edinburgh, which attempted to go further than the *St. James's Gazette* articles (reference 59 *supra*) which are reprinted in the *Dispatch*, 17 February, 1888, p. 4 and 20 February, 1888, p. 4. The 22 May 1888 article had been based on consultations with Francis Darwin, Dr. Ezard at the Royal Medical Society and the Edinburgh University Librarian. Its anonymous author had searched the Jameson papers in the University Library and had tried to trace Darwin's landlady. He had found very little. From all this, it seems most unlikely that anything new of value will subsequently be discovered about Darwin's residence in Edinburgh.
72. Jacques Barzum, *Darwin, Marx, Wagner*, London, 1942, p. 90.
73. Anthony Quinton, 'The Neglect of Victorian Philosophy', *Victorian Studies*, Bloomington, Indiana, I, 3, March 1958, p. 252.
74. H. W. Rutherford, compiler, *Catalogue of the Library of Charles Darwin, now in the Botany School, Cambridge*, Cambridge, 1908.
75. Ronald L. Meek, 'The Scottish Contribution to Marxist Sociology' in *Democracy and the Labour Movement*, ed. John Saville, London, 1954, pp. 99-102.
76. Last paragraph, Chapter XIII.
77. Herbert W. Schneider, *A History of American Philosophy*, New York, 1946, p. 166.
78. Ibid., p. 165.
79. Grant, op. cit., p. 342.
80. E.g. Thomas Brown, *Observations on the Zoonomia of Erasmus Darwin*, *M.D.*, Edinburgh, 1798, pp. 460-7.
81. Cf. Duncan Forbes, 'The Rationalism of Sir Walter Scott', *The Cambridge Journal*, VII, 1, October 1953, p. 34.
82. Francis Darwin, *Life*, op. cit., I, p. 40.
83. Ashworth, op. cit., pp. 110-112; Cossar Ewart, op. cit., pp. 17-20.
84. Francis Darwin, *Life*, op. cit., III, p. 300.
85. Alexander Wilson and Charles Lucian Bonaparte, *American Ornithology*, Edinburgh, 1831, I, pp. xiii-lxxxvi.
86. Saunders, *Scottish Democracy*, op. cit., pp. 252-253.
87. Cf. Michael Gelfand, *Livingstone the Doctor*, Oxford, 1957. Livingstone's interest in Darwin and his theories is seen, for example, in *The Last Journals of David Livingstone in Central Africa*, London, 1874, ed. Horace Waller, I, 19-20, 311-12.

88. W. H. Marwick, 'Patrick Matthew', *Scottish Adult Education*, Galashiels, 23 August 1958, pp. 20-22.
89. Krause, op. cit., p. 81.
90. Since this paper was written, four books have appeared in connection with the Darwin centenary which throw additional light on Scottish influences on Darwin: Loren Eiseley, *Darwin's Century*, London, 1959, see especially pp. 144-8 on Robert Grant; Gertrude Himmelfarb, *Darwin and the Darwinian Revolution*, London, 1959, see especially pp. 22-4 which suggest that there may be a little more manuscript evidence of Darwin's Edinburgh period than reference 71 above indicates; *Forerunners of Darwin, 1745-1859*, ed. Bentley Glass and others, Baltimore, 1959, passim; and Milton Millhauser, *Just Before Darwin. Robert Chambers and 'Vestiges'*, Middletown, 1959, passim. The most important work which recognizes the Scottish ideological background to Darwin's thought is Charles Coulston Gillispie's *Genesis and Geology* (reprint, New York, 1959), which was not available to me at the time this paper was written. Dr. Gillispie's book deserves the attention of all who are interested in what has been, until recently, a neglected period of Scottish intellectual history.

LANCELOT HOGBEN

Darwinism and Human Society in Retrospect

In recent times, physique has equipped few men more felicitously than Charles Darwin and Karl Marx to fulfil the role of father figure. Devoted followers of each have fathered on them views which they could not possibly have entertained in their life times unless endowed with second sight. Such has been the destiny of many others, notably Newton; but judicious appraisal of Newton's contributions in his own generation did not arouse passions which a discussion of the views of Marx still excites, and those of Darwin at least till lately excited. Happily, one can now re-examine Darwin's credentials before an audience that attained intellectual maturity after the controversy over his teaching had begun to cool off.

SCIENTIFIC KNOWLEDGE AND IDEOLOGIES OF THE PERIOD

To get the major issues sharply into focus, certain facts about the material circumstances and mental climate of Darwin's time are highly relevant. Of the former, three are most significant. During the thirty years before the *Origin of Species* appeared:

(a) oceanic navigation under steam power had both greatly enlarged opportunities for a global survey of living beings and forced the problems of geographical distribution on the attention of naturalists;

(b) surveying of the type initiated during the period of canal construction had received a new impetus from railway construction.

(c) optical technology had borne fruit in cardinal improvements both of the microscope and of the telescope.

The first of these signalised the acquisition of a heretofore undiscussed body of data challenging, if only because of their novelty, to traditional views concerning the origin of the contemporary diversity

37

of animal and plant life. The second had equipped the collector of fossils with contour maps confirmatory of the general picture of the formation of the earth's crust first advanced by Hutton in the context of a precocious outburst of evolutionary speculation to which Erasmus, the grand father of Charles Darwin, had contributed. Before 1810, there was little or no basis for anticipation of rational grounds for presuming an orderly succession of new types throughout a period of time vastly greater than the duration of the written record of human existence. By 1860, the principle of geological succession was a commonplace.

In the same milieu, advances of optical technology are revealing in a different sense. In its own time, the microscope which accompanied Darwin on the *Beagle* was not despicable, though by modern standards fitting only as a Christmas gift for an 11-year plus. Darwin himself was about twenty years old when the newer microscopes bore fruit in Amici's discovery that one pollen grain fertilises one ovule, and when Cuvier assigned the human sperm as a parasitic organism to the genus Cercaria in his *Regne Animale*. The reproductive processes of *Cryptograms* then justified their designation. Why few zoologists in 1850 accepted the doctrine that one animal sperm fertilises one ovum sufficiently explains why no zoologist—not even Darwin or Wallace —recognised the wider implications of Mendel's work published ten years after the reading of their joint communication. Modern methods of fixation began to come into use during the fifties; but there were as yet no microtomes which could take advantage of the fact. The numerical constancy of the chromosomes was unrecognised. Indeed, Hertwig and Fol gave the first ocular demonstration that only one sperm fertilises one ovum some fifteen years after the *Origin of Species* appeared; and the date is especially eloquent because any intelligible meaning we now attach to the term biparental inheritance in a biological context is referable to the material contribution of the sperm and the ovum to the outcome of the developmental process.

The three material features of the setting for the revival of evolutionary speculation at the end of the fifth decade of the nineteenth century have special interest if we also recall that it happened at a time when three major controversies dominated the ideological scene:

(a) Well into Darwin's manhood, wellnigh all the English leaders of natural science—Faraday and Joule as well as Davy, Henry, Dalton and Priestley before them—being noncomformists, had no university training. The Godless College was nonexistent in Darwin's boyhood, and a Test Act excluded nonconformists from Cambridge till ten years, from Oxford till twenty years, after the *Origin* appeared. Indeed, throughout nearly the whole of Darwin's lifetime, the rival claims of ecclesiastical and secular control of the educational system at every level was the focus of bitter controversy.

(b) The repeal of the Corn Laws occurred twelve years before the celebrated joint communication, and throughout the greater period of Darwin's lifetime the notion of free competition as a social ethic was the focus of a secular controversy debated with scarcely less vehemence than the right of the Bishop's bench to censor a curriculum of naturalistic studies.

(c) Darwin could recall the abolition of the British slave trade during his boyhood, and had started his professional career as a naturalist in the Royal Navy before the prohibition of slave ownership in the British Colonies. The Abolition controversy was at its height during the decade which ended with the appearance of the *Origin*. The American Civil War began within four years of this event, and each side had vehement supporters in Britian.

With the end in view and with the space at my disposal, it is not possible to dovetail all these clues to the impact of the *Origin* on his contemporaries. So I shall say no more about the relevance of the *laissez faire* controversy to the peculiar appeal of the Malthusian jingle in the disillusion subsequent to the bright hopes of the French physiocrats. Nor shall I discuss at length the comic irrelevance of Herbert Spencer's beatification of natural selection as the Survival of the Fittest. In retrospect, Corn Law Darwinism has too corny an aspect to merit comment in the contemporary context. Of planning we may say what St. Augustine said of the City of God: *petant aut non petant venire habet*. In short, we are moving into a more planned society, whether we like it or not. That human nature need or should be red in tooth and claw is not consistent with the ostensible aspirations of modern men, unless we flatter the White Settlers of Africa by designating them as such.

On the other hand, we cannot judiciously assess the effect of Darwin's teaching on the discussion of racial questions, if we regard the issues involved as exclusively factual or logical. Biologists of the mid-nineteenth century approached them with social preoccupations intelligible only in the context of theological debate. Indeed, a brief digression on the Test Act situation in its own technological setting will usefully emphasise how exiguous were the logical ties between what Darwin asserted and contemporary interpretation of his teaching, the more so because the *Origin* evoked no controversy conducted with comparable vehemence in contemporary France, where men of

39

Lancelot Hogben

science in the tradition of the *Ecole Polytechnique* were mostly *libres penseurs*.

THE DOCTRINE OF EVOLUTION

In its own social context, we have seen that technological advances had made possible considerable advances of scientific knowledge contributory to a formidable body of geological and geographical data which a Biblical view of creation, upholstered by Paley's natural theology with a teleological rationale, could not readily co-ordinate in a framework congenial to a sceptic. In the same *milieu* as the Test Act controversy, the untimely intervention of Bishop Wilberforce against so astute a champion as Thomas Henry Huxley at the British Association meeting of 1860 set what was to be the pattern of a debate which proceeded for more than a generation within the framework of common acceptance of a stupendous *non sequitur*. Thenceforth, both contestants subscribed to the dual proposition: if Darwin and Wallace are right, Genesis is wrong, and if Genesis is wrong, Darwin and Wallace are right.

The first half of the proposition is unexceptionable, but the second is silly unless we concede that there are only two conceivable accounts of the origin of the diversity of living beings. It is therefore pertinent to remind ourselves that evolution is not the bare statement subsumed by the factual assertion embodied in the historic principle of geological succession. The doctrine of evolution makes the *additional* assertion that the divergent succession of living types is a consequence of the two circumstances incidental to the normal process of generation now subsumed by the terms hereditary transmission and genetic variation. In fact, as earlier remarks on the role of the microscope have sufficiently emphasised, it was not yet possible in 1859 to formulate clearly what we mean by the distinction, and it was wholly impossible therefore to produce experimental evidence in support of the addendum.

Doubtless Darwin, who discreetly kept in the background of what was essentially an ideological controversy little to his taste, sensed this deficiency. At least, he followed up his masterly assemblage of facts invitatory to speculation on origins at a new level of discussion by publishing an anthology of domestic varieties of animals. For two reasons, we can say without hesitation in retrospect that *Animals and Plants under Domestication* adds nothing conclusive to the debate from a scientific, in contradistinction to an ideological, viewpoint. One is that most, if not all, of the data are susceptible to the interpretation that new domesticated varieties have arisen by recombination of highly diversified gene complexes through crossing

40

different inter-fertile local varieties; and the possibility of change through such a process in the absence of mutation terminates automatically when we have extracted all viable re-combinations. The other circumstance that deprives the argument of cogency depends on whether we define species in terms of what botanists sometimes respectively call a Linnaean and a Jordanian species. The latter include inter-fertile geographical varieties, but the former include units which either produce sterile offspring or no offspring at all when mated *inter se*. Darwin's data with reference to animals and plants under domestication throw no light whatever on how bisexual forms can arise, if inter-sterile with parent stock in this sense.

Only during the last half century have we gained conclusive proof of the mutation process, and only in our generation have we obtained clear-cut evidence that new forms inter-sterile with parent stock can arise without supernatural intervention. Otherwise, as was recognised by Phillip Gosse—father of Edmund Gosse and himself a professional geologist—we are free to interpret the historical record of the rocks as an indefinitely protracted sequence of acts on the part of a suppositious creator. As a devout Plymouth Brother, Phillip Gosse conceived the time scale of the sequence to be commensurate with the majesty of Jehovah with full scriptural authority for the assertion that a day is with the Lord as a thousand years. On this understanding, anyone with a flair for the esoteric use of language can accommodate the facts as then known with a poetic interpretation of the Pentateuch narrative.

The vagueness of the species concept, as Darwin's zoological contemporaries used the term, casts a long shadow over the discussion of inter-fertile local varieties of *Homo sapiens* in the ideological context of the Abolition controversy. Taxonomists had not—and have not yet—resolved the antinomy of natural and artificial classification at the level discussed so informatively and inconclusively by Whewell in the first half of the nineteenth century. The popularity of evolution exonerated them from further discussion of the issue in terms of the adequacy or inadequacy of a traditional two-valued logic by endowing the task with a new and, as we now see, unattainable objective which condemned zoology to wander for forty years in a barren wilderness of phylogenetic speculation. In the exhilarating climate of emancipation from Paley's natural theology, transitional types, whose intrusion into an otherwise tidy taxonomy had hitherto been a liability, had now the assurance of a cordial welcome as missing links. In short, Darwin's followers regarded the best arrangement of species within genera as an arrangement which mirrors phyletic relationships. By the same token, they equally condoned the pro-

Lancelot Hogben

priety of discussing which inter-fertile local varieties within a species are more or less ancestral. Fortified by the belief that human fatigue is the only obstacle to the elucidation of such pedigrees by recourse to anatomical data, taxonomists undertook this heraldic task with no misgivings about the outcome.

Indeed, it will be difficult to believe that such a hope could have sustained such stupendous persistence in fruitless and trivial exploits of repetitive mensuration, if we do not fortify our credulity with the reflection that persons of considerable intellectual standing, including Alfred Russel Wallace and Karl Marx, enthusiastically subscribed to the cult of phrenology when craniometry was still in the cradle. Even so, early measurements should have sufficed to damp the ardour of the most credulous craniometrician, if rational considerations had any relevance to the issue. The cranial capacity of Bismarck was 1,965 c.c. and his brain weighed 1,867 grams. The cranial capacity of Leibnitz, who advanced mathematics as did few others of a very creative period, anticipated the study of comparative linguistics, and managed the financial affairs of the Elector who founded our own Hanoverian dynasty, was 1,422 c.c. and his estimated brain-weight was 1,257 grams. The figure for cranial capacity is instructive when placed side by side with that of La Chapelle Man (1,620 c.c.) and a mean figure for Eskimos cited as 1,563 c.c.

GEOGRAPHICAL AND RACIAL ISSUES

How lately such considerations influenced discussion of the geographical distribution of human endowments is evident from an autopsy on a Carnegie Institution publication by Davenport and Steggera,[1] widely quoted at the time, and based on a study of 372 Jamaicans chromatically classified by the authors as Blacks 105, Whites 100 and Browns 167. By that time the I.Q. had come into the field as a serious competitor to craniometrical precision. From the study of samples not too sizeable to exercise scrupulous attention to the method of social selection employed, the authors arrive at *inter alia*: (a) the encouraging conclusion that Whites were 'outstandingly superior in their ability' to detect ridiculous conclusions, since they did best in Test No. III (answer to 'common sense' questions), No. IV (meaning of words) and No. V (reconstruction of pied sentences); (b) the discomforting disclosure that the Blacks excelled in Tests No. 1 (following complicated directions), No. II (problems in mental arithmetic), No. VI (recognising and continuing numerical series), and No. VII (logical relations and analogies). The authors successfully talk their way out of this dilemma by asserting

42

(p. 469) that 'the Blacks seem to do better in simple arithmetic and with numerical series' because 'it seems a plausible hypothesis for which there is considerable support that the more complicated a brain, the more numerous its association fibres, the less satisfactory it performs the simple numerical problems which a calculating machine does so quickly and accurately'. It is almost impossible to attribute a mischievous intention to any authors whose criteria of reasoning are so sub-standard.

Both contemporary genetical considerations referable to repetitive and back-mutation at the same locus, and palaeontological evidence of the extent of convergence in the past, have now taught us to dismiss the possibility that we can ever hope to tailor the terminal twigs of a taxonomic system to a historical sequence; but the illusion that it is possible to do so undoubtedly gave a powerful impetus to the discipline we now call physical anthropology. Reference to the literature of the sixties abundantly discloses that one circumstance propitious to this was the hope of demonstrating that the African negro is more primitive in a zoological sense than the Southern gentry and their supporters. Whence we are to conclude that: (a) the African is less teachable; (b) the African is not entitled to use the ballot box; (c) the African is a suitable beast of burden for the white man. Each of the last three statements is a *non sequitur*, though little recognised as such in the highly impassioned climate of debate at the time of the American Civil War and its aftermath. Today, it suffices to say that the hope which sustained the undertaking is itself illusory.

A humane man, who expresses in his Journal profound disgust towards the institution of slave ownership, Darwin bears no responsibility for this perversion of his teaching. It is also relevant to recall that the *Origin* appeared before the publication of the microbiological researches of Koch and the immunological studies of Pasteur. Only during the last fifty years have parasitological investigations familiarised us with a host of data relevant to the question: what obstacles have retarded the technological deveopment of the African peoples? Of itself, the fact that domesticable ungulates in general, and the horse in particular, are highly susceptible to trypanosomiasis has condemned Africans south of the Tropic of Cancer to be their own beasts of burden in territories where malaria,* yellow fever, hookworm infection, schistosomiasis and many other diseases only lately recognised by medical science exact a heavy toll from the vitality of the people.

---

* One often hears from those who should know better that natural selection has made the African immune to *malaria*. In fact, malaria is a major menace to inhabitants of the African village in the early years of life.

In the highly charged emotional climate of the Test Act controversy, thinking about the race issue was also liable to distortion for a reason, which Disraeli's memorable phrase recalls. In short, the uprisen ape was not after all a fallen angel. Provoked by the irrationalities of their opponents, biologists thus found themselves sorely tempted to justify the inclusion of Man in the animal kingdom by recourse to arguments more menacing to the credentials of their antagonists than relevant to the rationale of a taxonomical preference. Inevitably in the heat of debate, it seemed all-important to emphasise what Man shares with other animals, the more so because so much about Man's peculiarities eludes what we ordinarily agree to call physiological inquiry.

To be sure, they had then good reason to believe that differences with respect to the genetic make-up of animal species are primarily responsible for differences of behaviour which distinguish one (e.g. a social ant) from another (e.g. a solitary bee). Thus the analogy between locally restricted species of social organisms with distinctive anatomical *facies* and human communities distinguishable both by different culture patterns and by minor somatic peculiarities such as skin colour or hair, disposed of any embarrassing temptation to remedy lack of intensive study of what is peculiar to the human ecological system.

Nor need we blacken the good name of our illustrious forefathers for what should now seem to be rashness of judgment on such matters. Our situation is otherwise. No one with educational pretensions still subscribes to John Lightfoot's chronology, which dated the appearance of human life on this planet at 9 a.m. on September 12th, 3928 B.C. With Lightfoot and Bishop Wilberforce so far in the rear, and with no less detachment than that with which our predecessors could examine what distinguishes the mussel or the marmot as one animal species from all others, we ourselves ought now to be ready to ask: what distinguishes Man from other animal species? Admittedly, we have still far to go before we can comprehensively discuss in the language of physiology the characteristics which make Man unique: but we shall not fulfil our target requirements unless we recognise what they are.

In broad terms, they are easy to state and commendably biological considerations do not discharge us from the obligation to do so. Man is uniquely educable. In a unique sense, Man is a tool-making organism. In a unique sense, Man is also an animal capable of informative communication through speech. Because of this threefold uniqueness, a single animal species can fashion a changing environment and hence a changing *milieu* for its own developmental process. Like any other organism. Man transmits his genes to the next generation; but for the three reasons stated, and in a sense which likewise transcends anything comparable that we may rightly say of any other species, Man also transmits experience to the next generation.

THE HUMAN ECOLOGICAL SYSTEM

Thus every change of the human environment through human interference signalises a new accretion of transmissible experience and a new potential of further change. Because of this, human society is a unique ecological system. It owes its essential peculiarities to idiosyncrasies on which the study of social Hymenoptera has little or no bearing. While there is admittedly a prima facie case for the assumption that other local differences of animal behaviour are finally traceable to differences within the proper province of genetics, there is no such case for the presumption that different patterns of Man's social behaviour are predominantly traceable to the same source.

In the last resort, the mutation of chromosomes or of single genes is admittedly the pace-maker of organic evolution. We now know what circumstances determine its tempo and character. These are: (a) the rate of mutation; (b) the viability of mutant types *vis-à-vis* the immediately available environment or the secular changes of the latter; (c) mating systems more or less propitious to the concentration of genetypes in pure lines in a particular ecological niche.

We now know, though only since 1920, that mutation rates are highly variable. Consequently, the circumstance that many species have remained in all detectable ways fixed throughout vast geological epochs confronts our view of the evolutionary panorama with no enigma. Darwin's contemporaries and immediate successors preferred to ignore it. More especially as interpreted by Romanes and Galton after Weissmann had discredited the Lamarckian superstition, the exponents of Natural Selection presented evolution as a process of ubiquitous, continuous and uniform change. Accordingly, the possibility of social change without concomitant organic change of comparable magnitude seemed to be contrary to the Laws of Nature. On the other hand, the possibility that Homo sapiens is from the genetic viewpoint a relatively stagnant species is no-wise repugnant to what we now know as surely as we also know that the human ecological system has a *momentum sui generis* regardless of concomitant selection of genotypes. No reasonable and informed person doubts that human beings are genetically variable; but a rational examination of the relation of transmissible patterns of human behaviour, both to the diversity of the external environment in time and space and to the systems of mating peculiar to local communities, must take within its scope a multi-dimensional potential of variation attributable to the circumstance that one generation passes on to the next its own experience and the experience of its predecessors.

A single example should make this manifest. If the beginnings of civilisation testify to the formative role of the calendar in the first stages of writing, they also disclose, and with equal eloquence, how latitude, climate and contour have been peculiarly propitious or otherwise to the universal necessity of time-keeping in communities which have refined the technique or have failed to do so. Though we still know very little about the genetic endowments of human communities and most that we hear is suppositious, such manifest external circumstances favourable to cultural efflorescence and to cultural stagnation are manifold. Nor can we appreciate how vast a range of possibilities they endorse if we discuss them singly and in isolation from the sum of acquired experience on which a particular community can draw. When different migrations of human stocks bring them into similar circumstances, it will rarely if ever happen that two communities will respond within a comparable framework of traditional behaviour and equipment. Whether new circumstances are favourable to human inventiveness or otherwise, and if favourable with what possible outcome, is an engma which therefore subsumes vastly diverse admissible solutions.

Thus the interplay of the diversities of environment on the stock-in-trade of transmissible experience encompasses a wide range of possibilities *vis-à-vis* the tempo and character of social change. Indeed, the inertia of experience accumulated in dealing with a stimulus-complex which Toynbee calls the challenge of the environment may more or less effectively resist the impulse to deal with a new stimulus in a new way when other means of doing so are available. Accordingly, one may cite numberless examples of how failure to take advantage of a new situation may then deprive a community of the means of meeting the challenge of a different and later situation. For instance, the consequences of first access to abundant root crops, or of migration into an area where domesticable ungulates are for the first time available as beasts of burden, may be quite different according to whether the event antedates or follows the establishment of a cereal economy. Equally, adoption of a maize economy may be attended by peculiarities—some of them medical—different from those associated with a millet economy.

A little reflection on widely accessible and abundant sources of information should, therefore, suffice to justify the conclusions that the joint relation of the human personality to its social and physical

46

environment admits of many degrees of freedom, that minor variations of the sequence of otherwise similar stimuli may lead to widely divergent responses, and that anticipation of future consequences from definitive antecedents is rarely (if ever) a profitable undertaking. That the human ecological system has unique features, that it has a well-nigh limitless potential of change in the absence of the operation of forces which make some animal and some plant species more short-lived than others, and that genetic variability is never manifestly the pace-maker of such change are indeed propositions attested by the proper study of mankind. No knowledge we have yet gained from the study of plant or animal breeding can nullify them. Accordingly, such knowledge is not necessarily relevant to the evaluation of the changing character of human society. It would be rash to deny the possibility that genetic selection has played a part in the decline of civilisations, as asserted by R. A. Fisher and the late Alfred Rosenberg; but it is reckless to assert that it has done so without a searching examination of other possibilities, the more so when an assertion seemingly relevant to a particular local situation embraces the history of all civilisations.

Are we then to conclude that biology can make no contribution to the elucidation of circumstances contributory to the diversity of culture patterns more or less highly characteristic of human beings with predominant physical attributes in a particular locality in a particular epoch? Assuredly not, unless we concede the impertinent claim that genetics embraces the entire field of biological enquiry, or subscribe to a still too widely current nineteenth-century attitude to technological progress in antiquity. In the first fine flush of an unprecedented sequence of inventions following the introduction of steam power and the elucidation of the electric current, it was easy for archaeologists to take an unduly teleological view of the origins of the use of fire and of implements, clothing, the calendar, writing, and especially (as the term implies) the domestication of animals. If we dispense with the inclination to do so, we are free to regard advances of human technology during the greater part of the 25,000-year saga of our species as a succession of fortuitous blunders dictated by unforeseen circumstances. In so far as this may be true, the *Führerprinzip* drops out of the story as an irrelevant postulate.

BASIC PROBLEMS OF SPECIES RELATIONSHIPS

We have then to re-examine from two points of view the meaning of what we have hitherto called domestication *vis-à-vis* the role of commensalism in the diversification of what I have here called the human

Lancelot Hogben

ecological system, meaning thereby what biologists customarily mean in contradistinction to the parochial and restricted use of the term in the title of the Professor of Human Ecology in Cambridge University. The beginnings of this composite system of species relationships take us back to the association of Man with inter-fertile local varieties of Canidae in the early Palaeolithic. What was mutually a commensal relationship thereafter endorsed the possibility of blundering into herdsmanship where: (a) hunting nomads accompanied by their dogs came into contact with gregarious ungulates; (b) there were natural barriers to circumscribe an inclosure in which to round up a herd. From one viewpoint, we may therefore ask how the inclusion of one species in the ecological niche we call a local culture determines the subsequent inclusion of another. For instance, we may plausibly examine the sequence: given grain storage, then mice or rats, then the cat.

From a different viewpoint, we may ask: what new mechanical problems does the inclusion of a new species in the human ecological system force on the attention of the social group? For instance: is it a mere coincidence that the indigenous Americans were without horses and had not perfected the wheel when Europeans came to their continent? In *Habitat, Economy and Society*, Daryll Forde has commendably put before us many problems of this type; but there is still considerable scope for fruitful co-operation between archaeologists, cultural anthropologists, zoologists and botanists in the search for answers to many others. In my view, we shall advance little towards a deeper understanding of the diversification of human culture patterns in space and time till we are able to answer them. To be sure, human ecology in the restricted sense of the term as used by the Medical Faculty of Cambridge has its own role to play until we know far more than we know as yet about what obstacles to technological advance are attributable to harmful organisms as members of the human ecological system in the wider sense of the preceding discussion.

On the other hand, the time is long overdue to recognise that the discipline designated physical anthropology, conceived in any terms other than its relevance to stocktaking in the tailoring and furnishing trades, is a blind alley in the landscape of biological science, like its parent phrenology harmless as a hobby for the opulent aged, but with no rational claim to support from the public purse.

REFERENCE

1. Davenport C, B. and Steggera, M. *Race Crossing in Jamaica*. Carnegie Institution, Washington. Publication No. 395. 1929.

W. STARK

Natural and Social Selection

It is, I think, only a slight exaggeration to say that in the social sciences the second half of the nineteenth century was predominantly a Darwinian age, just as it is justifiable to call the second half of the eighteenth century a Newtonian period. Biology was the undisputed Queen of the hour, and it is understandable that all the other sciences should have tried to participate in her prestige and to bask in her reflected glory. Nothing is less surprising, then, than the rapid rise, and the equally rapid spread, of that important school of socio-logical thought which has come to be known as Social Darwinism. But the transfer of Darwinian modes of thinking from nature to society and culture created considerable difficulties, difficulties not always fully appreciated at the time. There was a great and decisive question which every intending Social Darwinian had to ask himself before he could take a single step further, and that question was, whether social life shows us the same processes of selection which Darwin had proved to be present in natural life, or whether society was not rather a suspension of the Darwinian struggle for survival, an enclave of peace as it were in a world of war. Both alternatives were fully developed in the literature, although in my opinion without sufficient attention to the tremendous initial problem involved. There sprang up two different Social Darwinisms, one positive and one negative, and their assertions, and even their researches, tended to cancel each other out. We can conveniently study the one in Otto Ammon's book, *The Social Order and its Natural Foundations*, and the other in Georges Vacher de Lapouge's book, *Les Selections Sociales*.[1] Ammon gives us essentially a picture of social evolution, of *up*ward movement, Lapouge a theory of social *in*volution, of downward development and decay, but both are Darwinians in the proper sense of the word.

49

THE OPTIMISTIC ALTERNATIVE: THE THEORY OF EVOLUTION

The silent presupposition from which Ammon seems to start is the assumption that the laws of nature formulated by Darwin are absolute in the most stringent meaning of the term. Men cannot abrogate them for any length of time, and we must consequently expect to find in society processes of selection which identify and exterminate the relatively unfit, just as we do in nature. Ammon distinguishes in the main three such processes, of which one is to all intents and purposes identical with the mechanism of natural selection, while the other two are, to say the least, parallel to it. Natural and social selection coincide, in so far as the struggle for the trough is concerned. Ammon was, like Darwin, deeply influenced by Malthus. There is a constant discrepancy between the number of hungry mouths on the one hand, and the number of loaves and fishes on the other. Hunger, the most fundamental of all biotic drives, forces us to compete with our fellow-men for the always insufficient supply of food, and in this struggle the marginal lives are invariably wiped out. This is nature's great method for the correction of her mistakes, and it operates on the human level as well as on the subhuman. The two more specifically human processes of selection are the school and the law. Ammon does not absolutely deny the educational function of these two institutions, but he regards the school in the first place as an agency for the detection of the mentally dull, not for their upbringing, and the law as an agency for the detection of the genetically criminal, not for their improvement. In the style of Galton and Lombroso he believes that dunces and criminals are born, not made, and that they must be got rid of, if the genetic quality of the population is not to deteriorate. He does not and he cannot admit that schooling may enlighten the stupid or punishment reclaim the lawbreaker: this would be assuming an indeterminacy in human life which simply does not exist, for all is in the grip of iron laws of which the laws of selection are an integral part.

Perhaps this theory which, as nobody can deny, is genuine Darwinism, is less interesting and significant in itself than the three corollaries which Ammon draws from it. If the fit and the unfit, the good lives and the bad, are essentially different streams of heredity, then we must expect them to be distinguishable by physical characteristics, and Ammon set to work to find out what these characteristics were. Being basically a physical anthropologist, he went and measured the height, size of head, length of nose and so on of the people of his immediate environment, the then Grand Duchy of Baden, and when he tabulated and digested his figures, he came to very curious results.

He found, for instance, that the upper classes, that is to say, those who are obviously successful in life and consequently fit for survival, were taller and more longheaded than the lower classes, those less successful in life and consequently less fit. This result filled him with enthusiasm because it was easy to link it with the basic teachings of physical anthropology. Physical anthropology has come to divide the Caucasian race into three sub-races—the Nordic, the Alpine and the Mediterranean. The Nordics are characterised by particularly tall stature and particularly egg-shaped skulls, just like the upper classes of the Grand Duchy of Baden; the Alpine people are particularly short-legged with billiard-ball-like crania, just like the lower classes of the Grand Duchy of Baden; what inference more justified, Ammon thought, than the conclusion that the nordic strain is exceptionally well-equipped by nature, in other words, genetically more valuable than any other, that in the Nordics we have before us Nature's finest achievement, whereas the Mediterranean and Alpine sub-races are, comparatively speaking, less successful experiments. 'Only and exclusively'—Ammon writes—'only and exclusively the type of man who has developed in the north of Europe with its inclement climate under the influence of hunting, of war and of knightly exercises offers those endowments which constitute the glories of the Aryan race, namely strength, energy, bravery, self-appreciation, love of truth, sympathy for the weak and genuine humanity.'[2] We are clearly confronted here with one of the roots of the ideology which dominated Germany between 1933 and 1945, but which was by no means restricted to Germany or the European continent alone. We find considerable traces of it in Anglo-American literature. It may be urged that racialism is not a legitimate offspring of Darwinism, that it does not by any means follow logically from the classical Darwinist position. Perhaps so. But the connection between the two is certainly not gratuitous.

A second corollary which Ammon drew from his basic Darwinism was a definite anti-egalitarianism. If natural processes of selection constantly polarise the population, make the wheat rise to the top and the chaff fall to the ground, then any step towards equality must necessarily be unnatural and consequently dysgenic. Ammon sees at least four reasons why a class society is better than a class-less one. In a class society all children can receive the education best suited to their hereditary equipment. No money is wasted on vain attempts to educate those who cannot be educated. In a class society all members can procure the food best suited to their natural way of life. The upper classes will consume the prime cuts which they need if they are to do all the brain work, and the lower classes the coarse meat which is

W. Stark

far better for those with menial jobs. In a class society the best elements in the lower strata—those to whom the accidents of heredity have given higher qualities than to their brothers and sisters—will have every incentive to exert themselves, to rise above their original station and to establish themselves among the upper ten. These three arguments carry considerable weight with Ammon, but I suspect that he ascribes most importance to the fourth. A class society avoids what Weismann describes as *panmixia*—*Anglice* indiscriminate interbreeding. Endogamy—marriage within your own set—is a usual feature of class societies. But this means, in Ammon's view, that the best will marry the best and the worst will mate with the worst. The worst will then degenerate and soon disappear, whereas the best will become even better than their parents, and there will result an upward breeding of the race. Herr Himmler's famous *Zuchtburgen*, where the attempt was made to bring together the *élite* of the SS with appropriately tall, egg-headed and blond maidens, was one of the implementations of the theory.

But we see its impact on the history of the twentieth century even better in Ammon's third corollary. He condemns all humanitarianism lock, stock and barrel, and I do not think that he is anything but consistent in this attitude. To keep those alive who are inherently dysgenic and whom nature has marked down for destruction is a stupidity which will drag its own condign punishment after it. For a while the laws of nature may be infringed, but ultimately they will assert themselves with a vengeance. The country which has protected its weak against the cold but bracing air of competition, which has, for instance, fed them at the expense of the strong and healthy, fed them out of a food supply which is insufficient to fill the stomachs of all, will go to the wall in the next war. And there will always be a next war. If life is, as Darwinism assumes, a struggle for survival, then every nation will sooner or later be tested in that great crucible and only those who have obeyed Nature's first command—that the fit should live and the unfit die—will emerge victorious from the contest. We see here looming up behind Ammon, not only Herr Günther who provided the Nazi philosophy, not only Herr Himmler who put it into practice, but even the gas chambers of Buchenwald and Auschwitz which were meant, in the spirit of this whole philosophy, to help Nature to do her 'wholesome' work.

THE PESSIMISTIC ALTERNATIVE: THE THEORY OF INVOLUTION

This tendency from biological theory to social theory, and from social theory to social practice, was powerfully strengthened by the influence of Vacher de Lapouge, the man, who, as I have indicated, started from the conviction that social selection is not, like natural selection, positive, but negative; in other words, that it preserves, not the best lives, but the worst. One can perhaps characterise the difference between Lapouge and Ammon by saying that for Ammon deviations from what is normal are only incidental and always short-lived, whereas for Lapouge the whole of society, its very being and its entire history, are the sustained attempt to defy and invert the laws of nature, a supreme *hubris* which can end only in a supreme catastrophe. Lapouge distinguishes eight processes of social selection which have this much in common that they all tend to change the genetic composition of the population for the worse.

As a true Darwinist, he puts war first. When a war breaks out, the most patriotic of men, the warrior types, spring to arms as soon as the call to the colours is uttered. Not so the cowards who hang back and often know how to avoid their national obligation altogether. No wonder that they survive, while the patriots, who never spare themselves, who volunteer for every dangerous mission, who always rush into the thick of the battle, are killed for their pains. Every war leaves behind more bad lives and fewer good ones. But the same decimation of the best goes on in peace time as well. Politics is, according to Clausewitz, a continuation of war with different means, and so it must have the same effects. Under a dictatorship both the dictator and his opponents will naturally be men marked out by nature for leadership. Tragically, they will try to exterminate each other. The dagger and the noose will take their toll, and so many born leaders will be wiped out. In democratic countries the situation is different. Violence is unknown, but the game will go against the best lives all the same. Who wins all the prizes in democratic countries? The demagogue, the man who is best at lying and deceit. Who goes to the wall? The honest man, the man who sticks to the truth. It is: heads I win, tails you lose.

Religion is a third agency which leads to the progressive de-naturalisation and degradation of the human race. Not all religions are equally deleterious, but Christianity belongs to the worst, and Catholicism is the very worst. All Christian denominations preach sex continence, and Catholicism insists on downright celibacy among her ministers. Those idealists who become preachers or priests consequently leave few offspring or none, whereas the lowest of the low, the dregs of the people, breed like rabbits. If every society is a mixture of water and wine, there is constantly more water and constantly less wine in the mixture. Morality has other implications as well, which push society further down the slope. Take such a seem-

53

ingly harmless habit as the wearing of clothes. Decent people insist on decent clothing, and thereby they keep the invigorating influences of sun and wind away from their bodies. The poor, who allow their children to run around half naked, are wiser in this respect. And then morality insists on the protection of the weak. It fosters the sentiment of compassion and the practice of charity, and this must act, and does act, like every other step away from and against nature. The unfit are preserved, and not only preserved, but enabled to breed. No wonder that they proliferate.

The fifth agency of social selection is the law, and in Lapouge's opinion it also works against the best. In this he disagrees most decidedly with Ammon. Many criminals, Lapouge insists, are not really criminals in the eyes of nature—they are criminals only according to the unnatural principles of our artificial codes. When we send them to gaol, we make it impossible for them to beget children. And the civil law is as disastrous in its effects as the criminal. Monogamy for instance means that even the best potential father can have no more than about one offspring per year. In nature that would be different.

Economic processes again weed out the good and make room for the bad. Nature's ideal type is the hero, but heroes have ever been poor money-makers. Under capitalist conditions the salesman with the glib tongue, the advertiser who is none too scrupulous about facts, and the speculator who has his eye on the main chance are the people who win the prizes. They can marry as soon as they like and raise families as big as they like. The decent people don't get on in such a world. They remain poor, and because they are and remain poor, they must postpone marriage and keep their families small. But this is not all. Where wealth is adored, many marriages will be based on financial considerations and not on physical attraction. Quite a few noblemen have married the daughters of rich bankers or stock jobbers, and this has done vital damage to the ancient aristocracies of Europe, and so to the whole human race.

Occupational selection is a seventh process that goes on in every society. The more skilled an occupation, the lower seems to be the fecundity of its members and *vice versa*. Irish migratory labourers have more children than Oxford or Cambridge dons. We get again the same picture: society is dying off at the top and proliferating in the lower branches.

Finally, there is the contrast between town and country. The towns attract the most active and the most energetic of the country people, those who are most go-ahead. And the towns are great killers. It is an old and often confirmed observation that the vitality even of the best strains is exhausted after three or four generations of city life, that they die off and die out after eighty or a hundred years. The great conurbations are bung-holes as it were through which valuable, nay invaluable human material is constantly being lost. And at the same time the yokels and the villiage idiots breed and spread their kind. Here again we have clearly negative selection, selection and survival of those who are least fit.

Every one of these eight processes would be bad enough in itself. But they go on side by side and so have a cumulative effect. There can be only one final result—the complete degeneration and annihilation of the human race. As Gobineau had expressed it before Lapouge: '[Racial] mixture . . . is the most obvious, the most certain, and the most enduring effect of the great societies and powerful civilisations . . . Once it has come about, the age of uniformity will begin . . . All men will resemble each other . . . They will all have the same amount of physical strength, similar directions in their instincts, and analogous gifts as far as their mental faculties are concerned, and this general level will bring the most revolting humiliation. The nations, or rather the human herds, weighed down by a dismal somnolence, will then lead a torpid existence, like the ruminating buffaloes in the stagnant mires of the Pontine marshes.' In the end, 'the globe, become silent, will continue to describe its impassive circles in space—but without us', without the human race. Race-mixture will have ended in race-extinction.[3]

THE SELF-CONQUEST OF SOCIAL DARWINISM

It is easy to see that the teachings of Lapouge, and of other, similar-minded writers such as Madison Grant with his book, *The Passing of the Great Race*, were bound to produce a state of acute anxiety in those who shared their fundamental ideas. Obviously, the rot had gone very far, and the only question was whether anything could be done at this eleventh hour to arrest it and to reverse the tendency. There was considerable doubt as to the possibility of this, but there was unfortunately no doubt as to the means to be applied. Ammon and Lapouge and all their friends were convinced that mercy was the culprit of the piece, the villain in this great drama of the human race. Mercy is unnatural—that seemed to the Social Darwinists the final upshot of the master's doctrine. Nothing is more revolting about the crimes and inhumanities of the second world war, the extermination of millions of people whose only fault was that they did not regard man as essentially a beast of prey, than the fact that they were inspired by, and committed in the name of, a great scientific theory.

55

There can be little doubt that Charles Darwin would have been horrified if he could have foreseen to what uses Darwinism would be put after his death. The question which the critical sociologist must ask is, of course, whether this whole extension of the theory of natural selection from the animal to the human sphere is justified, and it is possible, indeed, easy, to give it a simple, straightforward and convincing answer. That answer is *no*. Nor is this merely the answer which we give to-day. Even at the time when the influence of Darwinism was at its height, the great majority of sociologists and social philosophers rejected, nay, recoiled from, the doctrines of such men as Ammon and Lapouge. Social Darwinism in this narrow and specific sense of the word did not succeed in storming the citadel of social thought; it remained an unorthodox attitude for all the predominance of biological modes of thinking. The reasons for its failure are not far to seek. True, the human race is an animal species, and in so far as, or rather so long as, it is an animal species it must obey the same natural laws as all the lower creation. But man is not only an animal. There is, as Kant liked to express it, not only phenomenal man, man as science studies him, but also noumenal man, man as a moral agent. In other words, there is not only man in the grip of necessity, but also man with the privilege of freedom. Ammon and Lapouge and other materialists would have ridiculed these Kantian conceptions and called them self-contradictory. But they are not self-contradictory. The facts are merely more complex than Ammon and Lapouge realised. Society is neither part and parcel of nature, as Ammon assumed, nor yet is it clean outside nature, as Lapouge was inclined to believe. The truth is that the laws of nature—the necessities of nature—delimit a certain area within which man can freely follow his own purposes and enjoy the sweets of self-determination. We call that area culture. To judge the phenomena of culture by the realities of nature is absurd; it is simply illogical, and this is precisely what the Social Darwinists attempted to do. Of course, even within the realm of culture, there are at work certain processes of selection (if so one wishes to describe them): one society rewards economic achievement rather than artistic achievement, the other artistic rather than economic; one prefers realistic painting to symbolical, the other symbolical to realistic; and so on. But it is impossible to draw any kind of parallel between this sort of social selection and any sort of natural selection. Social selection (to stick for a moment to a term which does not really fit) takes place on the basis of values, whereas natural selection takes place on the basis of law. The two are as different as freedom and necessity.

This is the judgment of an unsympathetic, though not, I should like to emphasise, of a prejudiced observer. It seems to be borne out by the fact that the influence of Social Darwinism on technical sociology has not only been defeated by its enemies; it has—what is far more significant—also been overcome by its protagonists themselves. We see its self-conquest and self-destruction in the life-work of the man who was perhaps its most brilliant votary—Ludwik Gumplowicz.[4]

Gumplowicz's mind was not only keener than that of Ammon and Lapouge, it was also more open, and he knew far more about history than they ever did. Yet he started as an out-and-out Darwinian. Nothing is more characteristic of his outlook than the insistence that even the division of labour and the fact of trade must be interpreted in terms of the theory of the struggle for survival. Prima facie both the division of labour and the exchange of goods and services appear as acts of human co-operation but in reality they are, according to Gumplowicz, nothing of the kind; they are rather part and parcel of the continuous war of all against all. What does division of labour, that deceptive term, really mean? It means that some people ride on horseback and others crawl through the mire; that some crack whips and others feel them on their backs. Adam Smith has misled us in this respect; Charles Darwin has put us right. It is the same with trade. The prototype of all trade is colonial trade, the kind of trade in which a handful of glass beads is exchanged against a handful of pearls. There is precious little difference between it and open robbery. Both are acts of exploitation of the weak by the strong, all appearances to the contrary notwithstanding.

What Gumplowicz really wants to provide is a scientific—a Darwinist—theory of history and he finds this quite easy, at any rate as far as the beginnings are concerned, for wherever we turn, we find at the beginning, and as the beginning, one and the same fact—the fact of conquest: as long as a human race or tribe lives unmolested, nothing happens that would need recording; but it is not in the nature of things that this quiet pre-historic way of life should last for very long. The races must clash and fight, if for no other reason, than because they need grass and water for their beasts. Of course, there is really another reason as well: to make slaves, or, even better, to make slaves along with the acquisition of their lands, over whom and over which you establish yourself as a privileged and exploiting class, freed from the need for menial toil and able to live for the more pleasant pursuits of war, the chase, religious observances and culture. That is what happened everywhere; in China, where the aboriginals, the Miao-tse, were subjugated by the Mongols, in Persia, where the Tadshiks were subjugated by the Turkmen and Afghans, in Palestine, where the Canaanites were subjugated by the Jews, in India, where the Dravidians were subjugated by the Aryan invaders, and indeed in Britain, where the aboriginal Celts were defeated and enslaved by a series of fierce, warlike aggressors, culminating in the final catastrophe of 1066. The war over, the conquerors at once begin to organise their domination, and so it is that the most important of all social institutions, the state and the law, are born. Like the division of labour and the practice of trade, the state and the law must not be taken, at their face value, so to speak, for arrangements in the interests of all. They are nothing of the kind. They were meant to subserve, and they did subserve, only the interests of the race which had become the master race. Gumplowicz, like Marx, has a crude class theory, only that it is less sociological and more biological than that of Marx.

As far as the opening chapters are concerned, it is all rather plain sailing for Gumplowicz: he seems to have the facts on his side. Few scholars would deny that in the early stages of human development war is endemic and conquest of prime importance. But Gumplowicz originally maintained that the *whole* course of history was explicable in the light of Darwinism, even if this is not quite so clear for the later ages as for the earlier. War never ceases: it cannot cease because it is natural. At home, it is true, inside the individual states, peace seems to reign, but, Gumplowciz points out, this is not really so. What has happened is merely that the form of the struggle has changed on the domestic front. Instead of open fighting with murder and bloodshed, which are now impossible because of the law and the state, we have politics, which is once again interpreted, on the model of Clausewitz, as a continuation of war with different means. Gumplowicz was prepared to argue that, in this country for instance, the Tories were the party of the Normans and Labour the party of the Saxons, the party of the defeated in the original race struggle who were now trying to throw off the yoke which 1066 and all that had forced upon their necks.

All this is good Darwinism, and there would be many who would be prepared to argue that it is not only good but also legitimate Darwinism. It is not, to say the least, inadmissible, to interpret the doings of those whom Vico has called our semi-bestial ancestors in semi-zoological terms; it is perhaps also true that something of primitive life and conduct survived longer beyond the childhood days of our species than we are often inclined to admit. But the great question surely is what happens once a cultural life springs up and adds to men's lower or animal nature a higher and more specifically human nature—once man is so changed that we can regard him, not only from the phenomenal, but also from the noumenal point of view. Gumplowicz was a true scientist in the sense that he allowed nothing to influence him but the facts, and because he kept to the facts, and the facts alone, he was forced step by step to abandon his original Darwinism for a different theory, so far as *developed* society and *modern* history are concerned. Rarely, if ever, has the inner dynamism of a doctrine led so directly to its own overthrow and downfall as Social Darwinism did in the mind of Ludwik Gumplowicz.

As he looked over the events of the more recent centuries, it was increasingly borne in on Gumplowicz that the social process which dominated them was not the primeval fact of conflict and conquest (although these continue and war remains an ever-present reality) but a new fact, the fact of nation-building—the process of amalgamation as he also called it. Out of the Normans and the Saxons there arises by slow but progressive fusion, the English nation—the very largely though perhaps not yet fully unified English nation as we know it today. Disraeli was wrong when he gave his novel *Sybil* the subtitle *The Two Nations*, for the dividing line between the conquerors and the conquered of yore has been increasingly obliterated. Analysing this process of amalgamation, Gumplowicz distinguished three main strands in it. First there comes linguistic unification. A society, if it is to function, must have a common linguistic medium, and one of the original idioms must for this reason disappear. The Normans gave up their original Norse when they became masters of Normandy, and later, when they became lords over England, they abandoned the version of French which they had adopted for English. A second step in the direction of the modern nation is the emergence of a common religion. Atheist though he was, Gumplowicz appreciated that a common altar means a good deal. Not for nothing has the word communion a double meaning, one religious, the other sociological. But as a man whose world-view was rooted in biology Gumplowicz placed most emphasis on the third aspect of development, the emergence of a new composite race out of the original pure races. When a common state, a common law, a common language and a common religion have established themselves, intermarriage between members of the upper and the lower classes, between those of Norman blood and those of Saxon blood, will follow of course. Gumplowicz expresses the opinion that as yet the two streams of heredity have not sufficiently mingled, that the coming of a common blood is still a thing of the future. But for all that he acknowledges that we are on the way: the gap, if it has not closed already, is at any rate closing. Now, all this means a good deal. It means, expressed in non-Darwinist language, that the processes of culture heal the breaches which the

59

processes of nature have created, that culture is socially—humanly—constructive, whereas nature is—alas!—very largely negative and destructive. Gumplowicz admits this to a considerable extent. He acknowledges that what he calls the syngenetic feeling, i.e. the feeling underlying the unity of society, changes its character with the progress of history. Originally, in the primeval human horde or swarm, in the primitive clan or tribe, it is no different from the sentiment which informs a herd of elephants. It is natural, instinctive; there is a physical basis to it; it is prior to the social bond and makes it. But as the races coalesce and form between them nations, the syngenetic sentiment is unwittingly transformed. It becomes psychical; there is no longer a hereditary or genetic basis to it, but a mental and cultural one; far from being before social life and constitutive of it, the syngenetic sentiment of the modern nations grows out of it and is its fruit. Indeed, Gumplowicz goes so far as to say that it is an 'ideal something', a very un-Darwinist and un-biological statement. It is characteristic that he abandons the word 'race', as he comes to speak of more recent centuries, and substitutes for it the term 'ethnic group'. The reference of the word race is to heredity, to biology, and to nature, the reference of the term ethnic is to education, to tradition and to culture. This change in terminology alone implies—and proves—the total abandonment of the fundamental position of Social Darwinism. Gumplowicz has to all intents and purposes conceded that its tenets are inapplicable to the social reality of the modern nations. He ends by demolishing the house which he had meant to build and to make impregnable.

To Gumplowicz himself this was nothing less than a personal tragedy, especially as it led to an estrangement with his favourite disciple, Ludwig Woltmann, who stuck to a narrower and more uncompromising form of Darwinism, and it may even have had something to do with his final suicide in 1909. To us modern sociologists it contains a lesson of supreme importance—namely that our science will only become truly scientific, scientific in the best sense of the word, when we learn to free ourselves from the undue adulation and imitation of the natural sciences which has marred so much of the history of our subject. In that history, Social Darwinism was no more than a parenthesis, but we shall do well to remember it and to heed the warning which it holds out to us. Gumplowicz has set up two signposts of which the one points in the direction of error, the other in the direction of truth. He has made it easy for us to choose the right turning.

REFERENCES

1. *Die Gesellschaftsordnung und ihre natürlichen Grundlagen*, Jena, 1895; *Les Selections Sociales*, Paris, 1896.
2. p. 102.
3. Joseph Arthur Comte de Gobineau, *Essai sur l'Inégalité des Races Humaines*, vol. IV, Paris, 1855, pp. 346, 353, 354, 358.
4. Cf. *Der Rassenkampf*, Innsbruck, 1883, also *Rasse und Staat*, Vienna, 1875. Interesting in this context, though far more complicated, is also the case of F. Novicov, who, two years before his death, published a *Critique du Darwinisme Social*, Paris, 1910.

C. H. WADDINGTON

The Human Evolutionary System

Very soon after the publication of Darwin's work attempts were made to show how the development of human societies and civilisations could be explained in terms of processes similar to those which Darwin had shown to be operative in the sub-human world. Unfortunately, the discussion of the early social Darwinists did not prove very enlightening. Their influence was perhaps strongest in America. The school which flourished there around the turn of the century has recently been critically evaluated by Hofstadter.[1] The inadequacy of their account of social processes arose essentially from an attempt to apply to human societies a rather crude interpretation of the hypotheses which Darwin had advanced concerning the animal world. In particular an unhappy role was played by that most misleading slogan, 'the survival of the fittest'. It seemed to follow from this that the doctrine of natural selection implied that those who were most successful in society were necessarily more important for the furtherance of evolutionary progress than their fellows. The multiple imprecision which the phrase actually contains was only gradually realised.

THE CRITERION OF NATURAL SELECTION: HEREDITARY TRANSMISSION

We are all fully aware now that natural selection is not primarily concerned with survival, in the sense of the persistence of any single lifetime, or indeed in any sense in which it can be validly equated with success. Evolution is a matter not of single life-times but of the passage of generations. What is important for it is not survival but transmission of qualities to offspring. This is, indeed, of absolutely overriding importance; so much so that when we speak of those which survive, or, better, transmit, as being the fittest, we are really adding nothing to the statement that they transmit. Fitness in this context must be defined in terms of transmission. The doctrine of

63

the survival of the fittest becomes translated on analysis into the tautological statement that those individuals in a population which are most apt to leave offspring ('fittest') will leave most offspring ('survive').

With the breakdown of the early attempts to apply a crudely-interpreted Darwinism to social affairs, the two studies, the evolutionary biology of the subhuman world and the investigation of human societies, have tended to pursue different paths. Of course, sociology, like all other departments of human thought, has been profoundly affected by the general philosophical implications of the theory of evolution—the substitution of dynamic for static categories of thought, the interest in origin and becoming rather than in mere being; but the more technical biological theories, and the developments which they have undergone more recently in the hands of students of the non-human world, have been of comparatively little importance to sociology. The time has now perhaps come when it may be worthwhile to reopen the discussion of the relevance of our present understanding of biological evolution to the processes of human social change. It is not to be expected, as we shall see, that biology can provide answers for any of the problems of sociology; but it may be that the modes of analysis and the types of formulation which have been found useful in the study of animal evolution will suggest questions which it may be profitable for the sociologist to ponder in relation to his own subject-matter.

ADVANCES IN THEORY SINCE THE TIME OF DARWIN

The theory of biological evolution has made several advances of a fundamental character since Darwin's day. Perhaps the two most important, and the two which occurred earliest, were the more or less simultaneous realisation among biologists that the Lamarckian hypothesis of the inheritance of acquired characters could not be accepted as a general mechanism, and the rise of Mendelian genetics. In Darwin's day, biology possessed no proper theory of heredity. It was thought, in a rather vague way, that when two parents had offspring, their hereditary qualities came together and formed a blend in their progeny. Darwin realised that this would entail a rapid loss of individual variation, which would tend to disappear in a general uniformity. If this were to happen, there would be no raw material on which natural selection could operate, and the Darwinian mechanism would be rendered inoperative. According to the ideas of heredity current in Darwin's day, evolution demanded the operation of some system which engendered new hereditary variation as fast as cross-breeding led to its disappearance. Darwin, though with considerable hesitation, was tempted to find this source of variation in the effects of the environment, as Lamarck had suggested. But the accumulation of experimental evidence gradually made it seem less and less probable that characters acquired by interaction with the environment are inherited, until about twenty years ago this theory was almost uniformly rejected as incorrect. Since then in quite recent years a few scattered examples of phenomena have been discovered which could be interpreted in this sense. It is, however, still clear that, although in certain circumstances a character acquired by an organism during its lifetime may be passed on to its offspring, such a transmission occurs only in exceptional and particular circumstances. It is highly improbable that processes of this nature can play any large or important part in the main course of evolution.

MECHANISMS OF HEREDITARY TRANSMISSION

As this hypothesis gradually lost its attractiveness, the new discoveries of genetics revealed for the first time the actual mechanisms of hereditary transmission in the biological world. The demonstration that heredity is controlled by genes, which do not blend with one another but retain their own character except when they occasionally alter by the process of mutation, entirely removed Darwin's difficulty about the disappearance of hereditary variation in cross-breeding, and rendered unnecessary any reliance on Lamarckian theory as a source of new variation. It is on the facts of genetics and the conceptual framework which has been elaborated to account for them that the whole of our present understanding of biological evolution rests. We shall shortly have to discuss them in some detail. But before doing so it is necessary to point out that the history of evolutionary theory did not cease with the rediscovery and elaboration of Mendelian genetics. We have now reached a stage at which the discoveries of two other branches of biology are beginning to play a very important role, which will almost certainly increase markedly in the near future. These two sciences are the study of development, also know as experimental embryology, or, as I prefer to call it, epigenetics, and, secondly, the study of animal behaviour, sometimes known as ethology.

MEMBERS OF THE EVOLUTIONARY SYSTEM

The whole set of processes and mechanisms by which evolutionary change is brought about may be called 'the evolutionary system'. If we take into account the contributions of all the various branches of biology mentioned above, we have to consider the evolutionary system as composed of four main sub-systems. One of these is the 'genetic system', that is to say, the biological mechanisms by which hereditary variation is brought into being and transmitted from one generation to the next. Another sub-system may be called the 'epigenetic system', and comprises the mechanisms by which the specifications (or information) contained in the fertilised egg are translated into the form of the adult organism capable of reproduction. A third factor is the 'exploitive system', by which organisms may select out of the range of possibilities open to them the particular habitat in which they will pass their lives, and which indeed they will often succeed in modifying. Finally, we have the natural selective system, i.e. the pressures and stresses of various kinds originating in the environment, including the biological environment, which determine the success of the various individuals in achieving reproduction. These four sub-systems are, as we shall see, not separate from one another, impinging individually on the evolving animal, but are instead intimately interdependent, so that the whole complex forms a cybernetic system involving feed-back relations.

Before starting our consideration of human evolution it will be as well to say rather more about the nature of the biological process, and in particular to try to illustrate in more concrete terms what is meant by the use of such grandiloquent terms as cybernetics in this connection. The genetic and the natural selective systems are the two components of the total evolutionary system which have been most fully discussed. It will be necessary to consider the genetic system in some detail when dealing with its possible application to the mechanism of human evolution, but there are no new points of principle that need be brought out at this stage in the argument.

THE EXPLOITIVE SYSTEM

The exploitive system has not in recent years been so much in the centre of the stage of biological interest, but its operations are relatively easy to understand. Naturalists have described many examples in which local races, or recognisable varieties within a species, show a tendency to choose a particular habitat, or exhibit a specific type of behaviour which brings them in contact with some corresponding aspect of the environment. For instance, in the butterfly *Colias eurypheme* in California there is a white form which is particularly active in the early morning and late evening, whereas the more usual yellowish types do not show a preference for these times of day.[2] Investigations of laboratory animals have also shown that different strains may be characterised by behaviour traits which cause them to choose different habitats. For instance, a large population of *Drosophila*, consisting of a mixture of strains each of which could be recognised by the presence of some visible gene mutation, was released in a space out of which there were eight openings leading into compartments with all combinations of light against darkness, heat against cold, and wetness against dryness. The percentages of the different strains which moved into the various compartments were markedly different. The strains differed not only in their tendency to move at all (i.e. general activity) but some showed a specific tendency to go into certain types of environment rather than others.[3] Little attempt has yet been made to show conclusively that such preferences are inherited, but the fact that they are repeatable characteristics of particular strains indicates very strongly that they must have an important genetic component. There can be little doubt that if selection was exercised for or against a particular behaviour preference this trait would either be strengthened or weakened.

Another type of behaviour preference which may have important evolutionary consequence is that shown in the selection of sexual mates. Here again, naturalists and students of wild population have shown clearly that local races of animals may exhibit marked mating preferences, usually favouring mates of their own race. Similar differential mating preferences may be discovered in laboratory strains of a single species. In this case selection experiments have been made, and it has been possible to strengthen the originally weak tendencies within natural populations[4] and in laboratory strains.[5]

It is clear that such genetically-determined behaviour tendencies towards preferences for particular types of habitat or mate will strongly influence the kind of natural selective pressures to which the individual is subjected, and thus the operations of the genteic system by which his inheritable qualities are passed on to the next generation. This provides a typical 'feed-back loop'. The nature of the genes in the animal helps to specify (or provides information for) the nature of the environment, and the environment, by its natural selective action, then helps to specify the character of the genes which will be contained in the next generation.

THE EPIGENETIC SYSTEM

The manner in which the epigenetic system operates in evolution is perhaps not so obvious at first sight. There are two important features of the developmental processes of animals which are particularly important in this respect. The sequence of changes by which the fertilized egg becomes an adult animal always involves considerable interactions between neighbouring parts of the embryo; for instance, mesodermal structures may induce specific types of differentiation in the ectoderm with which they are in contact, the tensions of the developing muscles have an influence on the form of the bones to which they are attached, and so on. These mutual influences are often reciprocal and are highly complex. The result of their action is that the various organs and sub-systems which come into being have been to some extent moulded by each other, so that they tend to form relatively integrated systems, whose unity we frequently acknowledge by using the name 'organ'. The second feature of epigenetic processes of particular importance to evolution is the observation that they normally exhibit a subtle balance between flexibility and the lack of it. The flexibility is shown by the fact that an environmental influence impinging on the developing organism will often succeed in causing it to diverge, to some extent, from its normal course, and develop into an environmental modification; the organism develops an acquired character. But equally obvious is a certain lack of flexibility; development has a strong tendency to proceed to some definite end point. For instance, the adult tissues such as muscle, nerve, lung, kidney, etc., are quite distinct from one another and it is rather difficult to persuade developing cells to differentiate into something intermediate between these main types. Again, the animal as a whole will very often succeed in 'regulating', that is to say, in reaching its normal adult state in spite of injuries or abnormal circumstances it may have met during the course of its development.

Both these features, the tendency towards organisation and the balance between flexibility and the lack of it, are characteristics of the epigenetic processes of comparatively highly evolved forms such as the multicellular animals. The study of the simplest living systems has shown very clearly that the ultimate units of the developmental processes are syntheses of single specific chemical substances, carried out under the control of nuclear genes. One can detect these in higher organisms also, but in them the entities with which the evolutionist normally deals, such as the limbs, digestive system, hair and so on, are complex systems involving the interaction of very many unitary processes of synthesis. It is to the nature of the interactions between these unitary processes that one must look for an ultimate explanation both of the organised character of the resulting organs and of their tendency to reach one particular end-point. The system of gene-controlled processes seems to be such that it has a certain number of relatively distinct courses of change open to it. We may say that the fertilised egg comprises a set of genes and associated cytoplasmic material which gives it the potentialities for proceeding along one or other of a definite set of trajectories of change as time goes on. Such pre-determined time-trajectories of change I have proposed calling 'creodes'. Each creode must be thought of as having certain characteristics of stability (or rather of a quality similar to stability but involving time, which I have spoken of as homeorhesis); that is to say, the developing system will tend to move along a creode and will resist being pushed away from its normal course by influences impinging on it from outside. If these succeed in diverting it for a time it will tend to come back on to the creode when the disturbing influence is removed, though, of course, it may not always succeed in doing so completely, and then the organism, even when it becomes adult, will exhibit some modification or abnormality.

The relevance of this to evolution arises, in the first place, because there is likely to be some genetic variation in the stability-characteristics of the epigenetic systems of the different individuals in a population. Putting it in simpler terms, if a normal heterogeneous population is submitted to some environmental stress certain individuals are more likely than others to be affected and 'acquire a character'. Moreover, some will probably acquire characters which are more useful in furthering reproduction than those acquired by others. We shall have natural selection operating to increase the frequency of genotypes which enable their possessor to become adaptively modified to this stress. Moreover, the organising capacity of epigenetic processes makes it likely that the acquired character will be a relatively harmonious one. It will not be a matter of, for instance, getting large muscles but lacking large bones to go with them. Finally, we have to take account also of the resistance to change shown by epigenetic systems. If selection for increasing the efficiency at acquiring a character has gone on long enough, it may make the developmental system so ready to produce the modification in question that it continues to do so even after the environmental stress is removed. When that happens we can say that the genetic system has 'assimilated' the environmental character. The total result exactly mimics the effects which might have been attributed to a direct inheritance of acquired characters, although the mechanism by which this has been brought about depends on strictly orthodox processes, and is quite different from that usually envisaged by those who still believe in the Lamarckian hypothesis.

INTERVENTION OF NATURAL SELECTION

These points have been expressed in a theoretical manner in order to give them generality, but they do not rest on purely theoretical

69

reasoning. The fact that populations often contain genetic variation in the ability of the individuals to acquire characters; that they respond to selection for efficiency in this respect, and to selection for one particular type of developmental modification rather than another; and finally that such selection may lead to the point of genetic assimilation of the acquired character, have all been remonstrated experimentally.[6] The experiments also provided an actual example of a further consequence that one would expect to arise. As the genotype of an evolving population becomes moulded by selection for its capacity to react in a satisfactory manner with environmental stresses, it will have built into it certain creodes with particular homeorhetic characteristics. When new gene mutations now occur, by what we may consider random changes in the nucleoproteins of the chromosomes, the effects these mutations produce on the phenotype of the animals containing them will not be entirely random, but will be, to some extent at least, characteristic of the epigenetic system in which the gene is operating. We have here another example of a feed-back loop, one which ensures that the phenotypic alterations produced by mutation are not completely independent of the demands which natural selection is making on the evolving animal.

HUMAN EVOLUTION CULTURAL AS WELL AS BIOLOGICAL

It is now time to consider human evolution. The four-membered evolutionary system which has just been described must, of course, continue to operate in the human species, as in every other. However, the salient feature about man—perhaps one might say that it is his defining characteristic—is that he has developed, to an enormously higher degree than is found in any other species, a method of passing information from one generation to the next which is alternative to the biological mechanism depending on genes. This human information-transmitting system is, of course, the process of social learning. This gives man a second evolutionary system superimposed on top of the biological one, and functioning by means of a different system of information transmission. Most of the human evolutionary changes which seem of real importance to us—most, for instance, of the features which distinguish modern man from his ancestors of the Old Stone Age—seem to have been in the first instance produced by the action of the second evolutionary system dependent on social transmission. On theoretical grounds, one may be fairly confident that biological changes have been occurring at the same time, but it seems difficult to argue that they have been the primary variables in the process, and indeed it is not at all clear that they have any important relevance. It is, of course, an important task for human biology to attempt to elucidate the nature and magnitude of the genetic changes involved in human evolution. But this is only a part, and in my belief a subsidiary part, of the attempt to apply Darwinian or evolutionary thought to human affairs. The major task which confronts us now is to investigate the parallels and contrasts between the specifically human evolutionary system based on social transmission and what we know of the biological evolutionary system based on genetics.

Let us consider, then, the various factors which make up the biological evolutionary system, and see what parallels we can find for them in the specifically human evolutionary system. In biological evolution transmission of information from one generation to the next is in the main carried out by the genetic system. In this the transmitting event occurs at the time of fertilisation, when each parent contributes to the newly formed individual a set of hereditary units, or genes. These units are essentially quite separate from one another, but in practice they are usually associated together in groups, and that in two different ways. As far as the biological genetic system is concerned, the most relevant form of association is a quite contingent one, which depends on the fact that the genes are located on chromosomes. Their arrangement into groups of neighbours held together by the material structure of the chromosome is usually, though not always, more or less irrelevant to their functioning. Another type of association between genes arises during development. The formation of the different tissues of the body, such as muscle, nerve, etc., depends on the inter-related functioning of sets of genes. In a certain sense, therefore, each specialised tissue of the body represents the activities of a group of genes (or perhaps better, represents a group of gene activities), the association of the members of the group being in this case not at all a matter of chance, since it is essentially dependent on the way in which the gene activities interlock and interact with one another.

These epigenetic groupings of genes—that is to say, groupings which arise from their activities during development—are not reflected in the normal transmission of information between generations of animals by the genetic mechanism. It is relevant to the human situation, however, to remember that even in animals something more may be involved between generations than the standard genetic system concerned with nuclear genes. The mother always contributes to the new animal a relatively massive amount of egg cytoplasm. In some groups of animals, for instance in insects, during the matura-

71

tion of the egg in the maternal ovary a large amount of the contents of certain other cells, known as nurse cells, is bodily injected into the developing egg. These nurse cells could be taken to represent one particular epigenetic grouping of gene activities, which thus becomes to some extent transmitted to the next generation. Again, in many animals which bear their young alive there are formed, by developmental processes in the mother, mechanisms for passing into the offspring certain of the results of the activities of epigenetic gene-groupings in her body. For instance, substances from the maternal blood may be passed into the offspring through a placenta or similar structure. The most striking of such developments in the animal world is, of course, the development of milk secretion in mammals. We know several clear-cut examples in which transmission through such 'para-genetic mechanisms, as they might be called, can be shown to produce easily demonstrable effects on the offspring. Typical examples are the milk factor concerned with tumour development in mice, and the effects of the maternal body-size on the growth of the young embryo in reciprocal egg-transplantations between mammals of different sizes. In the subhuman world, however, the para-genetic mechanisms which can be utilized for transmitting to the next generation the results of the epigenetic interactions between genes are only rather slightly developed.

The situation is very different in the specifically human evolutionary system. The cultural, or as we may call it, the 'socio-genetic', transmission mechanism does not operate entirely or even mainly at one point in the life history of the new generation. There is no single entity that has to carry the message from one generation to the next as the gametes do in the biological world. We have, as it were, an enormous expansion and multiplication of modes of para-genetic transmission. An individual can receive information from his forebears throughout the whole, or at least the greater part of life, although, as we know only too well, the task of getting new ideas into his skull becomes progressively harder after a certain age.

This escape from the domination of a single major transmitter such as the gamete makes it possible for the socio-genetic system to handle groups of units which are associated, not only by chance as are the linkage groups of genes on the chromosomes, but which are grouped together by their functional interactions, in a manner comparable to the organized groups of gene activities which arise during development. If one were to attempt, therefore, to break down the content of social transmission into a series of unit items one should expect to find these items associated into groups in two rather different ways. Firstly, there are, of course, many functional interrelations between different items of transmitted content; the varied elements involved in a complex industrial technique, or the inter-related beliefs comprising one particular church doctrine, would provide examples. It is clear that the socio-genetic mechanism is quite capable of handing on such organised groups of units, the organisation being a functional one and comparable to that which characterises the tissues of an animal's body; that is, it is of a kind which in general is not capable of biological transmission to the next generation. But we might ask if there are also chance associations which could be regarded as comparable to the linkage between genes which happen to lie on the same chromosome. For instance, in the transmission of western culture to oriental nations it is very common to find that an item such as the wearing of western dress tends to be associated with other items such as various industrial techniques, or belief in the dogmas of Christianity. There is clearly very little essential functional connection between industrialism and the wearing of trousers rather than a sarong, dhoti or kimono. The association between such items, in so far as it exists, would seem to be a purely contingent one, quite comparable to that between different genes in a single linkage group. Social anthropologists seem in recent years to have been so interested in establishing the reality of the functional connections between elements of culture that the possible importance of purely fortuitous associations, comparable to those of linked genes, has perhaps been somewhat neglected.

GENETIC TRANSMISSION AND LEARNING

As a matter of fact subhuman evolution has involved not only the true genetic mechanism, and the para-genetic mechanisms such as transmissions through mammary secretions. There is a further subtlety, which is concerned with questions which almost merit the name of 'metagenetics'. As Darlington[7] in particular has emphasised, any particular mode of genetic transmission, for instance one depending on chromosomes and bisexual reproduction with cross fertilisation, endows the organisms which utilise it with certain capacities for evolutionary modification. Another mode of genetic transmission, for instance one in which the organisms are self-fertilising hermaphrodites, carries with it different capabilities for performing evolutionary advance. During the existence of living things on earth there have been, Darlington claims, alterations in these modes of genetic operation; there has been an 'evolution of genetic systems', as he terms it. The most important steps in this have been the organisation of genes into chromosomes, the adoption of bisexual

73

reproduction, and of course the evolution of the socio-genetic mechanism itself. But within the socio-genetic mechanism, once it has appeared, we can find a parallel process, an 'evolution of socio-genetic mechanisms'. In particular, there has been a development of phenomena of the kind which Bateson has called deutero-learning, that is to say, learning to learn. In this, the content acquired from the learning process is the ability to learn other things more quickly or more efficiently. This is an example of a second-order improvement in the mechanism of social transmission, comparable to the improvements (from the point of view of evolution) in the genetic system discussed by Darlington.

The development of deutero-learning introduces concepts which we might consider 'meta-socio-genetical'. There have, however, also been many evolutionary advances of a less radical nature in the socio-genetic system. They have produced alterations, which from the point of view of human evolution can in the main be considered as improvements, in the mechanisms of social transmission. Some of them have recently been discussed by Mead.[8] There is, for instance, a very primitive kind of social transmission of experience, which in fact many animals other than man also exhibit. In this, transmission occurs direct from individual to individual, through unverbalised behaviour of the teacher which conveys some inarticulate message to the learner, either as a model to be imitated or as a directive to some course of action. This primitive mode of transmission often persists as an accompaniment to the more highly evolved socio-genetic mechanisms. Posture, gesture, turn of phrase, stress and accent all convey whatever it is they do convey in this manner. Although it is primitive and undifferentiated, this mode of transmission is not without power. The characteristics which differentiate the products of the best public schools and Oxbridge from those of the secondary modern and Redbrick have been in the main passed over by this mechanism which man shares with such other social creatures as the red deer and the prairie dog.

The main defect of this model-mimic or leader-follower system of transmission is its relative inefficiency in handling items of information which are capable of being conceptualised. It can indeed transmit emotional or affective material which is by no means simple, but there is a great deal of human experience for which other systems of socio-genetic transmission have, it appears, proved much more efficient. The simplest of these systems can indeed be regarded as only a formalisation and extension of the inarticulate model-mimic arrangement. This is the apprenticeship system, in which teaching is still largely by showing and only partially in the form of words and formal instructions. Human apprentice teaching, however, differs from animal model-mimic transmission in such factors as the conscious utilisation of repetition as a means of indoctrination, and in its development of a long-term course of instruction leading towards a definite recognised goal. It is still utilised even in the most highly evolved societies at many levels of sophistication, from the training of a plumber or carpenter through that of a doctor or lawyer to the most rarified spiritual level of a guru and his pupil.

The next step in the evolution of socio-genetic transmission mechanisms is, perhaps, the formalisation of rote learning. In general, in modern societies rote learning is used to inculcate information which has somewhere or other been recorded in written form. This is the case, for instance, in the rote learning of the Koran or the Confucian classics which are features of classical Mohammedan and Chinese education. The existence of a written test is, however, not a necessary adjunct of rote learning. One might hazard the guess, for instance, that the bards of Homer's day, like the court singers of classical Ireland, Iceland and West Africa, to name a few cultures at random, were taught largely by rote with an almost total absence of any writing.

PROGRESS BEYOND PERSON-TO-PERSON TRANSMISSION OF LEARNING

It was, of course, the invention of writing which removed from the socio-genetic mechanism the necessity for person-to-person contact between the transmitter and the recipient. It is scarcely necessary, and certainly impractical in a lecture such as this, to elaborate the steps in the development of techniques of social transmission through recorded conceptual language. I will only make the remark—not entirely a facetious one—that impressive though these advances have been in some respects, we seem in some ways only too reluctant to take advantage of them. Why, the University teacher often thinks, must he continue to spend so much of his time using for the nth year in succession a technique of instruction which was sensible enough for his forefathers who had no alternative method available except manuscript treatises inscribed on vellum? Whereas, he nowadays could so easily record, not only his voice, but if you wish an accurate representation of his expression and gestures, on a piece of magnetic tape, while he himself wrote learned works in a villa in the south of France or conducted experiments in his laboratory.

It is characteristic of all the more highly evolved means of socio-genetic transmission that they do not depend essentially on person-to-person contact. The biological genetic system has of course never

75

escaped this limitation. Every individual animal must have an individual mother and the majority of them an individual father also. The major weakness of the biological system from an evolutionary point of view is that, although it ensures some mixing of hereditary qualities from different individuals, it limits the number of individuals which can participate in this mixing to only two; and in practice it usually operates to reduce the difference between these two since it is difficult to persuade mother and father of widely different kinds to hybridise. This tendency against hybridisation is very greatly reduced in the human socio-genetic system. One of the major features of human evolutionary processes, in fact, is the incorporation into one culture of elements which have arisen in another. The process is comparable to what is known in the botanical world as introgressive hybridisation. In the biological realm the results from a wide hybridisation usually differ from the original type not so much by presence or absence of individual genes, but rather by the persistence or loss from the strain of whole chromosomes. In the socio-genetic system of man also, when cultures come in contact it seems that what they take from each other is not a number of separate discrete items, but rather large portmanteau chunks of information. It is not, I think, quite clear whether these chunks are comparable to chromosomes; that is to say, are composed of a more or less randomly-associated set of items which happen to occur together, as do the genes in a linkage group on the chromosome, or whether the chunks are always more highly organised in a manner comparable to the epigenetically-interactive groups of gene activities which characterise the different tissues of an animal body. When one culture adopts from another, say, a religion such as Christianity, it is clear that we are dealing with a group of items which is organised and which is comparable rather to an epigenetic grouping than to a purely genetic linkage group. On the other hand, when the Indian culture adopts from the British such diverse items as a taste for cricket, a particular method of parliamentary election, a certain organisation of the army, and a special administrative jargon such as 'I beg you to do the needful', it seems rather more likely that we are dealing with the introgression of an arbitrarily associated group of items, comparable to the genes in a chromosome.

The varied items of information which are transmitted by these different mechanisms must have originated in some way when they first began their social career. It has been suggested above that in the socio-genetic system incorporation of items from other cultures (processes comparable to introgressive hybridisation), and the transmission of complexes of units whose unity is essentially epigenetic, are both much more frequent and important processes than the comparable happenings in the subhuman biological system. But they cannot be the whole story of the origin of variation in the human cultural heritage. There must be some process by which new items of socially transmissible information are added to the human store. In biological evolution much of the genetic variation in a population is created anew in each generation by recombination of already existing genes, but we fully realise that this shuffling is essentially a second-order process, based on a primary process of mutation by which new alleles are created. What is the comparable process to mutation in the socio-genetic system?

The answer must be two-fold. In the first place, one may point out that in socio-genetics a process comparable to the inheritance of acquired characters undoubtedly occurs. Cultural transmission, as we have seen, does not depend on specialised transmitting entities, comparable to gametes, but the situation is as though any differentiated tissue of the animal's body could transmit its qualities direct to the next generation. Thus, much of the new variation in socio-genetically transmitted items can arise as acquired characters, from the interaction between the human beings in the population and their surroundings. The human evolutionary system can thus utilise a vast source of variation which is more or less closed to the sub-human world. But it is by no means certain that all new socio-genetically transmittable items arise in this way. Man appears to develop ideas whose nature is not a necessary consequence of the environmental circumstances, and in so far as this is the case, these ideas can scarcely arise solely as acquired characters. It is difficult, for instance, to deny that there is some arbitrary element in the distinction between the great religions, such as Christianity and Buddhism. There would seem to be a place in the genesis of new human ideas for some process which shares with gene mutation a characteristic of randomness and unpredictability.

We have recently come to realise that a very important property of the biological genetic system is the existence within natural populations of a tendency which has been called genetic homeostasis. A natural population of animals contains a pool of genes, the particular genetic endowment of any one individual being a sample drawn out of this pool. If some disturbing agency, such as natural selection, is applied to the population, the frequency of the various genes in the pool will be altered. The tendency of the population to genetic homeostasis is exhibited by the fact that when the selection pressure is released the frequencies of the various genes frequently return towards, or even reach, their original values. The genetic make-up of the population, in

F

fact, exhibits some resistance to agents which would tend to change it. A similar balance between a certain degree of flexibility combined with some resistance to modifying agents is, as we have pointed out above, also shown by the epigenetic systems which lead from the egg to the adult condition.

QUESTIONS TO THE SOCIOLOGIST

In the socio-genetic system there are parallels for both these types of qualified stability. In human culture, however, it is not so easy to distinguish between them. As we have seen, the socio-genetic system includes phenomena comparable to the inheritance of acquired characteristics and the transmission of epigenetically organised complexes. Thus there are several mechanisms by which a human culture can manifest resistance to change, but it is not easy to classify them in groups comparable to those which are applicable to the biological evolutionary system. One agent opposing change may be the mechanism of socio-genetic transmission itself; for instance, many cultural traits which are conveyed by the primitive inarticulate transmission mechanism, which was discussed first above, seem to be very resistant to change, probably because of the transmission filter through which they have to pass. Examples are the somewhat nebulous, but often easily recognisable, qualities which are often spoken of as national characteristics, such as Jewishness or Indianness. Here, perhaps the socio-genetic mechanism is producing something closely comparable to biological genetic homeostasis in its strict sense. At the other end of the range there are tendencies to stability in human culture which arise from what is clearly an epigenetic unity; for instance, a closely organised body of dogmas such as that of the Roman Catholic Church is not at all easy to alter and tends to be transmitted more or less unchanged from generation to generation. In between these two extremes there are very many intergrades. It does not seem likely that much purpose would be served by trying to classify them on the basis of their logical similarity to comparable genetic and epigenetic phenomena in biology.

There is in this general field one consideration about human society which does, I think, raise some interesting questions. Most animals retain only for a very short fraction of their lifespan any capacity to be modified by their environment. The period in which they are epigenetically flexible is comparatively short. Man can—indeed in the present century probably must—go on learning throughout practically his whole life. One might then institute a comparison between a whole generation within a given human culture and a single

animal individual, regarding the changes which the human generation undergoes during its lifetime as comparable to the changes
which the egg will undergo as it develops into an adult. One would
find then, I think, that what we may call the 'socio-epigenetic' system
of a generation varies considerably from culture to culture. In some
there is much more resistance to change during a given lifetime than
in others. In American culture, for instance, it is a matter of pride
that an individual should adopt new habits and modes of life as they
come along. In Britain, classical China, and many other countries
much more value is attached to clinging to the old ways. This is very
comparable to the fact that in animal species one can find some whose
development is extremely resistant to modification by the environment—is, in fact, what has been called strongly canalised—while in
others the epigenetic processes are much more flexible. For instance,
mice inhabit a very large variety of habitats, but look very much the
same in all of them, whereas some invertebrate species are so easily
modifiable that almost every pond in which they live has its own recognisable population. In the biological realm the strength and character
of the epigenetic canalisation can certainly be controlled by selection, and is a factor which plays an important role in evolution.
In the socio-genetic system the readiness to accept change within a
generation must also be both influenced by, and itself influence, the
evolutionary processes.

Closely allied with these matters is the problem which Darwin
made central in his work—the problem of speciation. It is an empirical fact that living organisms do not vary continuously over the whole
range which they exhibit, but that they fall into more or less well
defined groups, which are commonly called species. The precise
definition of what constitutes a species is a matter of great difficulty,
about which biologists are hardly yet in agreement, but that some
significant discontinuity occurs can scarcely be questioned. Para-
doxically enough, however, the origin of species is just the facet of
evolution on which Darwin's theories throw the feeblest illumination.
We still have very little understanding of why discontinuity occurs so
frequently. We have to suppose that in some way certain constel-
lations of hereditary potentialities fit together into a stable pattern,
while other combinations are inharmonious; but that is only a very
abstract and general statement. But, although biologists do not
understand it, here is an area of enquiry which, one feels, sociologists
will also have to face. To what extent is discontinuity a characteristic
of the variation between human cultures? To the outsider it would
seem that we find phenomena extremely similar to those with which
the biologist is familiar; some instances of sharp distinctions between

even closely neighbouring cultures, as in such a culturally diversified area as New Guinea; some examples of more or less continuous geographical variation, comparable to the formation of local races, in widespread cultures such as, to take an extreme example, the British with its offshoots in Canada, New Zealand, Australia, etc.; and a tendency, also familiar in biology, for the initial slight geographical variants to evolve into fully distinct 'species'. The dynamics of this process—for instance its dependence on, or independence of, the formation of barriers to cross-mating—would appear to present sociologists with problems very similar in their formal structure at least to those with which biologists are wrestling.

Finally, I think the biologist would wish to ask the sociologist whether there is in his system of ideas anything which plays the evolutionary role of natural selection. Something, after all, must decide which new items of culture, either adopted from other societies by processes akin to hybridisation or arising 'out of the blue' by some analogue of mutation, will succeed in persisting for many generations. Why, for example, were Christ and Mohammed accepted as Messiahs out of all the candidates for that role? Or why were Lamarck's and, for a long time, Mendel's ideas rejected while Darwin's won immediate acclaim? The processes are, perhaps, so complicated that we cannot hope to find any general portmanteau term like 'Natural Selection' to apply to them. But one wonders whether this is not too pessimistic a view. The natural selective value of a new biological variant depends on the number of its offspring. It is possible that the ability of a new cultural item to persist could be deduced from the magnitude of its cultural progeny—its ability to 'cross-breed' with already existing facets of the culture and to beget issue from them? And of course we should not forget that many biologists now attribute a considerable influence to the fluctuations of random sampling as a phenomenon which mitigates the rigours of strict natural selection. How great a role does pure chance play in the preservation or disappearance of new cultural items?

In making these remarks about human evolution it has not been my intention to suggest that our knowledge about the biological evolutionary system will enable us to answer the problems with which sociologists are confronted. All I have tried to show is that a number of quite interesting lines of thought emerge if one takes in turn each of the factors which we consider important in biological evolution, and asks oneself what corresponds to them in the human cultural system. Darwinism in its heyday seemed to some of its enthusiastic supporters to have all the answers on the biological level, and they were so convinced of this that they felt that it must also provide the answers in sociology. Nowadays, even within biology I think we are more modest. We may feel that Darwinism, as it has been modified and developed in the last hundred years, provides us with the main principles which we require for an understanding of biological evolution, but perhaps the most striking feature of the last two or three decades has been the realisation of how much still remains to be discovered. There are probably rather few biologists —though there certainly seem to be some—who would be confident in asserting that their science gives the essential key to the understanding of human affairs. But the modes of analysis used by the biologist may be at least suggestive to sociologists, and I hope that this attempt to look at their field from the angle of recent evolutionary theory will provoke thought, even if the result of that cogitation is to reject all the suggestions I have made.

REFERENCES

1. R. Hofstadter, *Social Darwinism in American Thought*. Revised ed., 1955, Beacon Press, Boston.
2. W. Horawitz *Symp. Soc. Exp. Biol.* 1952, 7, 238.
3. C. H. Waddington, B. Woolf, and M. M. Perry, *Evolution*, 1954, *8*, 89.
4. K. F. Koopman, *Evolution*, 1950, *4*, 135.
5. G. R. Knight, A. Robertson, and C. H. Waddington, *Evolution*, 1956, *10*, 14.
6. C. H. Waddington, *The Strategy of the Genes*, 1957, Allen and Unwin, London.
7. C. D. Darlington, *The Evolution of Genetic Systems*, 2nd ed., 1946, Cambridge University Press.
8. M. Mead, Cultural Determinants of Behaviour, in *Evolution and Behaviour*. ed., Simpson and Roe. 1958.

J. MAYNARD SMITH

Evolution and History

Sociologists tend to be suspicious of the application of biological ideas to their subject. So much nonsense has been written in the guise of 'Social Darwinism', and so many crimes justified by theories of racial superiority, that this suspicion is perhaps justified. Therefore I would like to stress at the outset what appear to me to be the limitations of biological thinking in the social sciences. I do not think that biological evolution has itself been an important motive force for change during human history, although it was responsible for the origin of those specifically human characteristics which made history possible. Doubtless the human species has continued to evolve throughout historical times, but at a rate which must have been very slow compared to the rates of historical change, mediated by cultural rather than by genetic transmission from generation to generation.

Nor do I think that the cultural differences between social classes, or between nations or races, are to any significant extent due to genetic causes. Social classes are seldom reproductively isolated from one another to an extent sufficient to permit any significant genetic difference to arise between them. This is not true of human races, which have in the past been sufficiently isolated for recognisable and genetically determined physical differences to arise, although physically distinct populations are usually connected by others of intermediate type. It is therefore conceivable that genetically determined differences in emotional and intellectual capacities may also exist. One reason for doubting that they do so is that the relative levels of cultural and technical achievement of different populations are not always the same at different periods of history. A genetic interpretation of history would require us to suppose that a thousand years ago the Arabs were genetically better fitted for scientific inquiry than the inhabitants of Western Europe, whereas today the reverse is true.

83

It is more sensible to suppose that the factors which influence the cultural achievements of a population are not to any great extent genetic.

In other words, genetically determined differences between human populations at different times or in different places can probably safely be ignored when considering the history of the last ten thousand years, although genetically determined differences between the individuals composing a society at any one time can not.

THE TWO USES OF ANALOGY

The main reason for applying evolutionary ideas to history lies in the hope of drawing helpful analogies between the two processes. Before considering some of the analogies which can be drawn, I would like to discuss in general terms the uses of analogy in science. Consider

FIGURE 1

THE ANALOGY BETWEEN MECHANICAL AND
ELECTRICAL OSCILLATING SYSTEMS

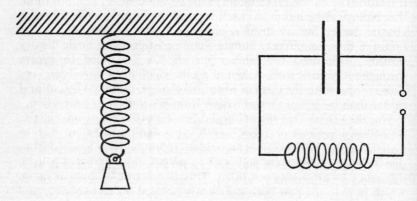

first a simple and well-understood analogy. Figure 1 shows two systems, one mechanical and the other electrical, which have in common the property of oscillating harmonically according to the equation $d^2x/dt^2 + Cx=0$, where the constant C depends in the one case on the stiffness of the spring and the mass of the weight, and in the other on the capacitance of the condenser and the inductance of the coil. The analogy between the two systems consists in the similarity in their behaviour, which in turn depends on the similarity in the relationships between their parts. It does not in any way depend on a similarity between mass and inductance as such. Two machines such as these, whose behaviour is identical, are said to be isomorphic.

There are two possible uses of such an analogy. First, if the analogy is exact it can be used for predicting the behaviour of one system by observing that of another. For example, since it is cheaper to build and to modify electrical circuits than complex structures, it was at one time the practice during the design stage to predict the natural modes of vibration of an aeroplane's wing by building an analogous electrical circuit; such a circuit was in fact an analogue computer. Today general-purpose analogue computers have been designed which, by alteration of their internal connections, can be made to solve a wide variety of problems. There seems little prospect that analogies between evolution and history will ever have a predictive value in this way. Even if it is possible to write down the initial conditions and mathematical equations which describe an historical situation with sufficient accuracy for prediction to be possible, it will always be cheaper to use an electrical than a biological computer to solve them. Unhappily, I cannot look forward to the day when the course of a trade cycle will be predicted by using populations of fruitflies or of bacteria.

But analogies have another use; they may help us to think about unfamiliar things. To return to figure 1, all human beings acquire during their childhood an understanding of mechanical phenomena, since they possess mechanical and visual receptors. Consequently, when first confronted with electrical phenomena, they find them easier to comprehend if they can draw analogies with more familiar processes. Most of us would, I think, admit that we found direct current circuits easier to understand by recognising the analogy between electrical potential and head of water. Perhaps there are some of you whose minds are sufficiently adept at abstraction to find such analogies unnecessary and therefore misleading, but I know it is not so in my case.

Now the use of analogies in this way is widespread in biology. It is not necessary that two systems be isomorphic, or that an exact mathematical description be given of either of them, provided that they have something in common in their behaviour. Examples of such analogies are the 'psycho-hydraulic' model of the brain evolved by Lorenz, and the comparison by Waddington of a developing organism with a ball rolling down an 'epigenetic landscape'. I do not know whether the former analogy has been useful, but I have during the last few years performed experiments which would probably not have occurred to me had I not been familiar with Waddington's model.

That analogies can readily be drawn between biological and social phenomena is apparent in such phrases as 'the head of state', 'arterial road' and 'the arm of the law'. If such analogies can be made more precise they may give us new ideas, although they cannot in the nature of things prove that those ideas are correct. But it seems to me that what we need above all else in the study of society is theories which we can test. There is nothing easier, either in biology or in sociology, than to collect facts not previously known. Almost any facts about human beings have an intrinsic interest for us, but the mere collection of facts, however interesting or however true, does not constitute science. It is an essential feature of the scientific method that we should put forward theories or hypotheses which are in principle capable of being contradicted by observation, and that we should then perform experiments or collect facts to see whether they do or do not contradict our theories. If the drawing of analogies can help us to formulate such theories, then it is justified. Some of the analogies suggested in Professor Waddington's essay in this volume seem to be of this nature. For example, he suggests that certain groups of ideas or customs may be transmitted together from one culture to another because they happen to occur together in the 'donor' culture, rather as genes may be linked on the same chromosome, and not because there is any necessary connection between the ideas and customs as such. This is a suggestion which is capable of disproof, and therefore informative. Does what a biologist would call the 'host' culture accept groups of customs merely because they are found together in the donor, or is it in fact selective, adopting only those customs relevant to its own conditions?

But although analogies between historical and biological processes can readily be drawn, I am doubtful whether any general analogy between them is likely to be helpful. In both, we are confronted by processes of continuous rather than of purely cyclical change. Also the behaviour of both systems depends on the interrelationships of entities which are not only very numerous (as they are in a crystal or in a perfect gas), but also of many qualitatively distinct kinds. Consequently the behaviour of both systems is of great complexity, so that theory cannot in general hope to predict the long-term behaviour of a system, but only the immediate effects of some interference with it. But when these general resemblances have been noted, I do not think that the two systems have much else in common. In particular, the ways in which the various entities concerned are interrelated are quite different in the two cases, as will become apparent if our current theory of evolution is presented in diagrammatic form.

In Figure 2, G represents the fertilised egg, A the adult individual

FIGURE 2

DIAGRAM OF THE THEORY OF HEREDITY

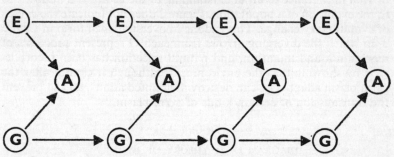

which develops, and E the environment in which it does so. The arrows from G to G represent Weissman's theory of the continuity of the germ plasm, those from G to A the process of development, and those from E to A the fact that the kind of adult which develops depends on

FIGURE 3

DIAGRAM OF THE THEORY OF EVOLUTION.

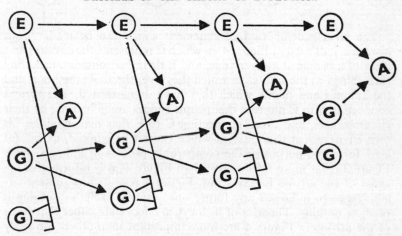

the environment. The absence of an arrow from A to G is commonly expressed by saying that acquired characters are not inherited, and the absence of an arrow from A to E implies that animals do not by their own activities alter their environment. This is of course not strictly true; but it is true that the influence of a population on its

87

J. Maynard Smith

environment is not usually of major importance either as a conservative mechanism or as a cause of evolutionary change, although it is often of vital importance to an understanding of the ecology as opposed to to the evolution of a population. Figure 2 does not indicate the causes of evolutionary change. This is done in oversimplified form in Figure 3, in which the diverging arrows from each G represent processes of segregation and mutation, and natural selection has been incorporated by showing that the environment, although it cannot alter the germ plasm adaptively, can destroy ill-adapted adults, and so prevent the transmission of certain kinds of germ plasm.

FIGURE 4

DIAGRAM OF A THEORY OF HISTORY

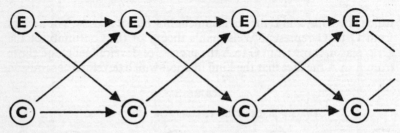

The most general kind of statement which can be made about history is indicated in Figure 4, in which C represents the customs and ideas of a people at a given time, and E their environment, including such things as the houses in which they live, the tools they use, and the animals and plants which they have domesticated. The arrows connecting E to C indicate that people's ideas are influenced by their circumstances, and those connecting C to E that man modifies his own environment to an extent which cannot be ignored, as can (at least for some purposes) the comparable process in animals. Now Figure 2 is far more informative than Figure 4; it is informative because of the arrows it leaves out. Figure 4 permits any present circumstance to influence any future one; since it excludes nothing it predicts nothing. Theories of history* in effect state either that some of the arrows in Figure 4 are more important than others, or apply restricted meanings to C and E, suggesting that some particular aspects of human behaviour and environment are of major importance in determining the course of history.[1]

* I omit what is perhaps the most popular 'theory', i.e. that no theory of history is possible: history is certainly very complicated, but that is no excuse for throwing up the sponge; evolution is very complicated too.

For example, Figure 5 shows two views of history which are formally similar to Figure 2; if either were true, useful analogies might be drawn between history and evolution. Figure 5a represents an idealist theory of history; what is important is the history of ideas, which develop according to their own logic, but which also determine the kind of world in which men live. It is not necessary to accept the Marxist thesis that man's being determines his consciousness to feel that this view leaves out too much to be helpful. Even a subject such

FIGURE 5

DIAGRAMS OF THEORIES OF HISTORY FORMALLY SIMILAR
TO THE THEORY OF HEREDITY

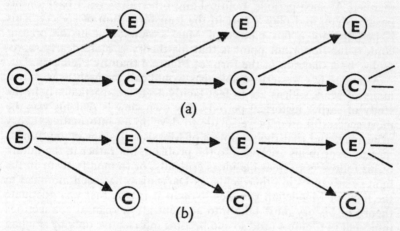

as mathematics, which is capable of considerable independent development in directions determined by its own internal logic, has been greatly influenced by problems of practice. Figure 5b represents a theory of 'economic determinism', which to the best of my knowledge has never been held by anyone, although it has frequently been fathered on Marx by his opponents.

THE MARXIST VIEW OF HISTORY

It is worth considering Marx's theory in more detail, since it was developed to act as a guide in changing society, and has in fact been widely applied for that purpose. It was avowedly a dialectical theory, and so does not lend itself to representation by diagrams which in effect describe the relationships between different parts of a machine.

J. Maynard Smith

However, Marx attempted to develop an informative theory from Figure 4, not by omitting some of the arrows, but by applying restricted meanings to the terms C and E. C represents the relationships between men in the process of production, and E the tools used in production. Marx suggested that the course of history was determined by the evolution of this sub-system, which he called the means of production, and which in turn influenced ideas of religion, philosophy, art and politics. Further, he suggested that the system represented by C, the social relations of production, show a greater conservatism than do the techniques of production. Consequently the social relationships come in time to act as barriers to the further development of production, and are then changed in a revolutionary manner. At such periods, political and other ideas react back on his basic system, and play a part in the transformation of society. This is perhaps not a fair picture of Marx's views; but in the present context the important point is that his theory is more nearly represented by a diagram of the form of Figure 4 than by Figure 5a.

Although few western sociologists would call themselves Marxists, many of Marx's ideas are in fact tacitly accepted, particularly in the study of earlier historical periods. My own view is that his was the most successful attempt yet made to develop an informative theory of history, and that the weakness of Marxism lies not in any fundamental error in his approach to the problem, but rather in the failure of his followers to treat his ideas critically, or to modify them in the light of advances in other fields, as Darwinism has been modified in the light of Mendelian genetics. Now if it is true that any adequate theory of history must take into account all the causal connections indicated in Figure 4 (and so can become informative only by singling out from the totality of events certain processes which dominate the course of history, either as Marx did or in some other way), then it follows that no formal analogy between historical and evolutionary processes as a whole is possible. In other words, I do not think that a helpful theory of history can be derived by starting from evolution theory, and attempting to find historical analogues for the various entities and processes involved.

THE PROBLEM OF CONSTANCY

Even so, it may still be possible to draw helpful analogies between particular aspects of the two processes. There is in fact one particular habit of thought characteristic of biologists which might usefully be borrowed by historians. Biologists are continuously interested in mechanisms which preserve constancy, of faunas, of species, of

90

individuals or of kinds of molecules. It would be interesting to know how far comparable mechanisms are responsible for preserving the constancy of human institutions and patterns of behaviour and belief. The constancy of human cultural patterns during the palaeolithic was extreme; for example, Acheulian 'hand axes' were manufactured with relatively little change for some 100,000 years over a large part of Europe, Africa and Asia. Such stability calls for an explanation. Or to take a more recent example, Gibbon once remarked that the curious thing about the Roman Empire was not that it declined but that it survived for so long. It may be that the search for the causes of constancy in human affairs may prove as fruitful as has the comparable study of homeostasis in biology.

In biology, we know of two rather different kinds of process for ensuring constancy, which I will call 'copying plus selection' and 'error regulation'. The conservatism of heredity appears to depend on the exact copying of DNA molecules, as a scribe might copy a manuscript. Since no copying process can be completely free of errors, this process would lead slowly but inevitably to chaos were there not some mechanism for eliminating the mistakes which are made. An error, called a mutation, is not corrected once made; it is eliminated by natural selection, or occasionally incorporated by selection in place of the original. In contrast, the physiological constancy of individuals is maintained by error regulation; if you get too hot you sweat, if too cold you shiver. The regulation of development appears to work in a similar manner, except that what is maintained is not a steady state but a particular pattern of change, which Waddington has called a creode.

It is easy to point to error-regulated constancies in society. The relative prices of commodities remain approximately constant through the action of the law of supply and demand. Or to take another example, it appears to be a feature of the present political systems of Britain and the United States of America that there should be two major political parties, of approximately equal strength, succeeding one another in office. I do not suggest that this is one of the eternal verities, but the balance has been maintained over an appreciable period. To explain this persistence, it would be necessary to show why it is that in time the party out of power gains support at the expense of the party in power.

The second type of mechanism, that of copying plus selection, seems to have no close analogue in human society. It is true that rote-learning is a copying process. But errors are not corrected by a selective process, unless we regard the failing of unsuccesful candidates as a form of natural selection. But it seems more natural to suppose that if errors of transmission occur, they are corrected so as to make sense, although not necessarily the original sense; to the best of our knowledge genetic mutations cannot be corrected so as to make biological sense.

LIMITATIONS OF ANALOGICAL METHOD

In conclusion, I would like to return to the comparison between Marx and Darwin. Darwin put forward a theory to explain how evolution had occurred. Marx put forward a comparable theory of history, but he claimed to have done more than this; he derived from Hegel categories of change which he held to be characteristic not only of history but of all natural systems, whether social, biological or physical. In the present context, this amounts to the claim that what history and evolution have in common is that both obey dialectical laws. Now there is no *a priori* reason why this claim should not be true, or, if true, why it could not be substantiated, as Engels attempted to do in *The Dialectics of Nature*. For example, many simple systems, mechanical, electrical and hydrodynamic, have the property of vibrating harmonically, and this category of behaviour could be recognised without making a detailed analysis of any particular case. Marx in effect claimed that dialectical categories of behaviour could be recognised as characteristic of more complex systems.

In a limited sense, most scientists would agree; for example, few use the phrase 'transformation of quantity into quality', but everyone is aware of the dangers of extrapolation. But is the dialectical approach of any more general value in science, and in particular in biology? I find this a very difficult question to answer. Often it seems to make simple problems complicated, and to substitute vagueness for precision. Occasionally it can have disastrous consequences. As will be clear from a comparison of Figures 2 and 4, evolution would be more like history if Lamarckian inheritance were true; if, in Figure 2, there were an arrow passing from A to G. This seems to have led some Russian biologists to defend what I believe to be an erroneous theory of genetics by the argument that it must be true because it is Marxist. Such an argument is a misuse of analogical thinking. If a scientist is convinced of the dialectical nature of history, it is natural that this should lead him to seek for comparable phenomena in biology, and perhaps to be predisposed in favour of a Lamarckian theory of genetics. But this in no way constitutes evidence in favour of such a theory, which can come only from observation and experiment, a point which was recognised by some but unfortunately not by all the participants in the Russian controversy. Analogies, Marxist or otherwise, may be helpful in suggesting theories, but are irrelevant when it is a question of confirming or disproving them.

There is however one very simple reason why a study of history may be helpful in suggesting ideas to biologists. Although historians may not yet have achieved an agreed theory by which to work, they know incomparably more about the actual course of history than biologists do about the course of evolution. Perhaps as a consequence, historians are obliged to recognise the dialectical nature of many historical processes, whatever words they may use to describe them, whereas most evolutionists are wedded to the 'inevitability of gradualness', a view which may be largely correct, and which in any case was held by Darwin. Perhaps the writer on evolution whose views would most appeal to a dialectical materialist was Richard Goldschmidt,[1] in particular in his views on systemic mutation, on the relation between organism and environment, and on the integration of the genetic material of a chromosome. There are features of Goldschmidt's views on systemic mutation which appear to me untenable. But he may have been right in thinking that evolution is a more dialectical and less Fabian process than many of us have supposed.

REFERENCES

1. R. Goldschmidt. *The Material Basis of Evolution*, Yale University Press, 1940.

MORRIS GINSBERG

Social Evolution

INTRODUCTION

It is difficult now to realise the strength of the impact of evolutionary
ideas on social theory in the period following the publication of the
Origin of Species. There is hardly a branch of social inquiry which
remained unaffected. As the historian Heitland said in 1924, 'We are
all evolutionists of sorts nowadays, though we differ widely in the
use we make of evolutionary principles'.[1] This remains true today
even of the critics of the theories of social evolution and of progress,
so deeply have ideas of growth and development come to pervade the
public mind.

To disentangle the various ways in which this influence has been
felt is a difficult task. The main directions, however, can be fairly
clearly distinguished.

In the first place the doctrine of the mutability of species, replacing
the earlier view of their origin in specific acts of creation, fundamentally altered the approach to society and culture. Religion, law, morals
which had generally been taken as fixed and given once for all, came
now to be looked upon as organs of society, serving human needs and
changing with them. No doubt notions of development had been and
were being advanced by philosophers and historians before the ad-
vent of Darwinism, but they came to be seen in a fresh light and were
given scientific warrant by the growing acceptance of Darwinian
ideas.

Secondly, the evolutionary approach and its instrument the comparative method brought out the unity of the human mind, that is,
the similarity of its structure in all its manifestations. The analysis
made by Tylor and Frazer of the cognitive structure of magical
beliefs and practices all over the world depended on the assumption that the modes of judgment and belief were everywhere the same

95

among men. It is true that they largely ignored the emotional and conational aspects of the mind, but there is no reason in later work to justify the belief that in these respects men are fundamentally divided. The attempt made by Lévy-Bruhl to draw a sharp distinction between the mentality of 'primitive' and 'civilized' peoples has not stood the test of criticism; and Lévy-Bruhl himself in his later writings agreed that though distinguishable, the two mentalities are not separated from one another by an unbridgeable gulf. What he calls the affective categories of the mind play their part at all stages, though in varying degrees.[2] One of the most impressive things in this context is the effect of the evolutionary approach on the study of religion. It is true that theologically minded students of comparative religion are still inclined to regard each their own religion as the culminating point in development. Nevertheless, they all insist on the spiritual identity of men everywhere and on the universality of the needs and aspirations which religions are taken to serve.

Thirdly, the stress that came to be laid on the old idea that societies are organic, or have organic character, served to emphasise the interdependence of social facts and relationships—an idea which lies at the root of all modern sociology.

Fourthly, and perhaps most important of all, is the general acceptance of the theory of mental evolution as a corollary of the theory of organic evolution. In a famous passage Darwin foresaw the effect his theories were to have on the study of mind. 'Psychology', he wrote, 'will be securely based on the foundation already well laid by Herbert Spencer, that of the necessary acquirement of each mental power and capacity by gradation'.[3] Since his day the growth of comparative psychology has amply fulfilled this prediction. The work of Spencer, Romanes, Lloyd Morgan, L. T. Hobhouse, to mention only a few of the pioneers in this country, and a host of students of animal and human behaviour in other countries, has brought out the continuity of mental evolution from the lower animals to man. There appear to be no unbridgeable gaps, no break of continuity either in the evolution of the nervous system or in the evolution of mental functions as revealed by the study of behaviour. I do not know of any evidence in recent work to throw doubt on the conclusion summed up by McDougall in 1925 in the following words. 'The parallel between the evolution of brain and the evolution of mental functions seems to be clearly made out, in general terms, as a rule without exceptions'.[4] It is difficult to over-estimate the significance of these lessons of comparative psychology for sociology. By all accounts the higher development of mental functions in man are in their nature social developments. The great superiority of the human mind to that of the

96

highest of the animals seems to be due in the main to the growing power in man of 'inter-learning' and of embodying the results of such learning with the aid of language and of artefacts in traditions handed on from one generation to another. From this point of view the study of social development may be considered as part of the wider study of the evolution of mind. I am not suggesting that all social development is mental development. But I do think that one of the key problems in sociological inquiry is that of the part played by knowledge of nature and of man in human history and of the relation between the growth of thought and of the development of ethical ideas and of social organization. The changes in the mental forces at work in society appear to be in the main independent of changes in genetic structure or racial type and accordingly their study though continuous will fall outside the scope of biology in a narrow sense of the term. On the other hand the close links between mental evolution and social evolution may well justify the view of those who hold that they can be treated as phases in the more general evolution of life and mind.

ORGANIC AND SOCIAL EVOLUTION

The word evolution has many meanings and it is not surprising that 'social evolution' has also been used in very different senses. Darwin himself described his theories with precision in the words 'descent with modification through variation and natural selection'. This describes both the fact of evolution and the processes whereby it came about. A more general definition might be that evolution is a process whereby groups of apparently different or independent entities such as species of animals and plants, chemical elements, or social institutions have been produced in the course of time from a much smaller number of parent entities. The element common to these different 'evolutions' would be descent with modification. The processes involved might, however, be different in the different spheres, different, for example, in the evolution of plants or animals and in the evolution of chemical elements or, again, of societies or elements of culture; and there might well be no general evolutionary theory implying that the different evolutions are stages in one universal process of evolution.

But evolution is also used to indicate a process of ascending advance towards greater multiplicity of parts and complexity of structure and function. Darwin seems to have thought that natural selection would operate in the direction of improvement of organization: 'The ultimate result (of Natural Selection) is that each creature tends to become more and more improved in relation to their conditions.

97

This improvement inevitably leads to the gradual advancement of organization of living beings throughout the world'.[5] I take it that 'improvement' means better adaptation to special environmental conditions and is not necessarily 'progressive'. On the other hand 'advance in organization' comes nearer the notion of progress as judged by other criteria. Among those that have been suggested by biologists are increased independence of the environment, or increased plasticity of behaviour or capacity for varied response to the environment. Recently J. S. Huxley has defined progressive evolution as consisting in 'improvements which permit or facilitate further improvements'.[6] As he explains, some such concept is necessary to indicate the process through which the 'higher' types come into being during geological time. As he further explains, such 'non-restrictive improvements' are rare phenomena, since most evolutionary trends come to a stop either through extinction or by passing into a stable phase. The point is important in view of the tendency among some of the earlier evolutionary sociologists to identify evolution with progress. Clearly retrogression, extinction, stagnation are as common in the social field as in other spheres of life. Not all evolution is progressive.

More far reaching are generalized theories of evolution such as that attempted by Spencer or more recently by the various forms of 'emergent evolution'. Spencer's evolution-formula according to which evolution is a movement from 'an indefinite unstable homogeneity' to a 'definite stable heterogeneity' was meant to apply to all spheres of being and is not now considered helpful either by scientists or philosophers. Theories of emergent evolution differ from Spencer's theory in making emergence of genuinely novel characteristics a general feature of the evolutionary process and not confined to one point, namely that at which consciousness emerges out of what was previously unconscious. There are on this view different levels of integration, each successive order involving a jump to something new, not deducible as a resultant from preceding modes of integration. Lloyd Morgan, for example, gives the following series: atom, molecule, colloidal unit, cell, multicellular organisms of increasing complexity, societies of organisms. He does not, however, inquire whether societies and especially human societies can in their turn be arranged in a series of ascending levels, and, if so, whether they are 'emergent' or not.

It is my intention here not to follow in any detail the various ways in which these three different but related concepts of evolution have been used in sociology, but to inquire what remains out of the controversies to which these efforts gave rise and when the strange exaggerations and aberration which they brought with them have been cleared away.

THE GROWTH OF LANGUAGE

First then, as to the concept of evolution conceived as descent with modification. In the cultural field the nearest analogy to evolution in this sense is to be found in the study of the growth of languages and in the history of tools. In the *Origin of Species* Darwin uses the analogy to illustrate what he calls genealogical classification (Ch. XIV). In the *Descent of Man* the parallelism between the formation of species and of languages is discussed at some length and reference is made to an earlier discussion by Sir C. Lyell in his *Geological Evidences of the Antiquity of Man* in 1863. Darwin shows that languages, like living beings, can be classed into groups; that in distinct languages there are striking homologies due to community of descent, and analogies due to similar processes of formation; that changes in letters or sounds are often accompanied by other changes in a manner very like correlated growth; that a struggle goes on between languages leading to the dominance of some and the gradual extinction of others; that within languages a similar struggle goes on leading to the survival of the fitter forms or elements; that distinct languages may be crossed or blended together; that both in languages and organisms the effects of long-continued use may be noted, and so forth. It may be added that as noted by P. G. Giles the idea that similarities between forms in different languages can be accounted for by descent from a common source was clearly formulated by Sir William Jones in 1786 a quarter of a century before Darwin was born, with reference to the similarities between Sanscrit, Latin and Greek, to which he added Gothic, Celtic and Old Persian. In commenting on the discourse in which this idea was developed Professor Giles remarks: 'No such epoch-making discovery was ever announced with less flourish of trumpets.'[7] Since that time, of course, the study of the relationships between different languages has been extended far beyond the Aryan group and attempts have even been made to show that all existing languages are derived from a single source. The issue between monogenesis and polygenesis is, however, still uncertain and most philologists consider that the question should be left open at present.[8]

THE HISTORY OF TOOLS

The fertility of the idea of evolution in the sense of descent with modification in the study of the history of tools is at least as clear as in

Morris Ginsberg

that of language. There is an elaborate morphology due to the labours of archaeological systematists and historians of technology. As Tylor remarked: 'The geographical distribution of these things and their transmission from region to region have to be studied as the naturalist studies the geography of his botanical and zoological species.' Darwin noted that in the case of language the process of change can often be traced with greater fullness than in dealing with animals and plants. A similar point is made by Tylor when he asserts that evolution is more easily verifiable in the study of culture than in biology. This is certainly so in dealing with tools and technological change generally, where continuity of development can often be traced with a completeness not achieved by biologists in tracing lines of descent.[9]

DIFFUSION AND 'PARALLEL' EVOLUTION

The use of the theory of evolution in the sense of the derivation of a series of entities from a common origin raises the problem of the role of diffusion in social and cultural history. This has given rise to a good deal of confused argumentation. Elliot Smith dismissed all forms of evolutionary theory other than that of diffusion from a single centre as a claim not for evolution, but for 'spontaneous generation'. But this seems to overstress community of origin and to neglect the role of variations in the evolutionary process. As I understand it the biological view now is that mutations may occur independently several times, and it seems that what is called parallel evolution may be explained as due to the occurrence of such mutations accompanied by parallel selection pressure. How much is to be attributed to community of descent and how much to similar processes of formation are questions within the general framework of evolutionary theory alike in biology and sociology and the answer may differ in different cases. There is nothing in recent work to invalidate the conclusions reached by Tylor that in accounting for any particular element of culture three ways are open: 'independent invention, inheritance from common ancestors and transmission from one race to another'. Only detailed historical investigation can decide between these three possibilities.[10]

RELIGIONS AND OTHER CULTURAL ELEMENTS

In realms of culture other than those of language and technology there are no systems of natural classification at all analogous to those which form the basis of the theory of evolution in biology. In dealing

100

with religion, for example, Tylor was interested in reducing the 'menagery of lower forms, variously classifiable as elves, gnomes, ghosts, manes, deities' to a few simple ideas which, as he thought, form the common groundwork of them all.[11] Others have concentrated on the classification of cults rather than of beliefs. But even today there is nothing like a generally accepted classification of religions. Those which are used by students of comparative religion, for example, the classification of religions into tribal, national and universal, or that based on their conception of the Divine, or the types of piety they foster are no doubt suitable for the purpose for which they were devised, but they are not very serviceable in tracing genealogical affinities. In any event, the significance of the evolutionary approach in the study of religion does not lie so much in following up lines of descent, as in the evidence it affords of the persistence of very primitive elements in the higher religions and of continuity of development. The major trends distinguished such as the gradual moralisation of religion or the trend towards unity, whether in the form of monotheism or of pantheism, fit more easily into broader theories of development than into theories of evolution in the sense of descent with modification.

Similar remarks apply to other elements of culture, such as legal and moral rules, forms of political organisation or of the family or systems of kinship. All these can be variously classified and major groups have been or can be distinguished. The analogy with biological species is, however, too slight to throw fresh light on the problems of development involved. It has to be remembered that whilst in biology the number of species that naturalists have to deal with runs into hundreds of thousands the number of distinguishable types of the state or of the family is very small. There is in fact only a limited number of possibilities in each case and rather than rely on biological analogies, it is obviously better to attack the problem in a direct manner by inquiring into the conditions that favour certain forms rather than others. It has to be remembered further that whilst in tracing descent outwardly observable similarities have generally to be appealed to, the deeper analysis of social structure involves reference to underlying principles and the mental forces at work, and these do not lend themselves to the sort of classification used by naturalists.

CONTRASTS IN SOCIAL AND BIOLOGICAL EVOLUTION

Passing now from the fact of evolution to the nature of the processes involved, we must, I think, accept the conclusion reached by T. H. Huxley in his Romanes Lecture on *Evolution and Ethics* delivered in

1893: 'That progressive modification of civilisation which passes by the name of the "evolution of society", is, in fact, a process of an essentially different character, both from that which brings about the evolution of species, in the state of nature, and from that which gives rise to the evolution of varieties, in the state of art'.[12] The essential processes in biological evolution are, I take it, variation, the inheritance of variations and selection. We can use these terms to describe social changes, but only by way of analogy and with important qualifications. Thus (i) social changes are in the historic period, in the main independent of changes in the germinal structure. As noted by Huxley, there have been vast changes in the structure of English society and civilisation since the days of the Tudors, but there is no reason for believing that this has been accompanied by any parallel changes in the inborn basis of the physical or mental character of the English during that period. So again it would be absurd to attribute the vast and rapid changes now occurring in Asian and African countries to changes in germinal structure. The changes are due to new orientation giving a different direction of intellectual activity and a different outlet for instinctive and emotional tendencies, an orientation which does not involve any change in the inherited structure. (ii) This independence from genetic changes makes social change far more rapid than biological change. A change in the structure of the family or in the class structure can be brought about in a few generations. (iii) Social inventions are far more intelligible than biological mutations. The sources of new ideas can often be traced in detail and the stimuli which arouse them can be investigated. (iv) Correlated growth was considered by Darwin 'mysterious',[13] and I suppose must remain a mystery till the causes of mutation are better known. In dealing with social changes the problem is not nearly so difficult, since a change in a part of the social structure can be shown to carry with it changes in other parts. Thus, for example, the invention of artillery had a profound influence on the social and political organisation of European states; changes in the industrial structure are reflected in changes in the structure of the family or the educational system. (v) Social changes, unlike biological changes, can often be explained as the result of co-operation as is best illustrated from the history of science and technology. In these fields the contributions made by different individuals are systematised by co-operative effort with results greater than any the unaided individual could attain. (vi) In dealing with social changes it is often possible to show how similar modifications appear in large numbers of individuals simultaneously. Quite apart from imitation, a change in circumstances may induce large numbers of individuals to act in similar ways. For example, in the period between 1300 and 1500 changes in the economic situation encouraged the practice of leasing land for life or for a number of years. In this way the older arrangements of tenure and service were steadily modified and the changes led eventually to the extinction of the system of tenants in villeinage. Thus a fundamental change in the rural economy was brought about by the actions of numerous individuals adopting a similar line of policy under a common stimulus. (vii) Finally the source of variation in social affairs is not nearly so mysterious as is the cause of mutation in biology. For in human life teleological factors are plainly operative. Changes are brought about by a process of trial and error and by deliberate effort directed to ends more or less clearly apprehended. Whatever be our view of the role of mind in organic evolution, there can be no doubt of its importance in social evolution.

INTERRELATION OF MIND AND NATURAL SELECTION

At this point the biologist might retort that conation and purpose are activities centred in some mind and mind itself grows up under the conditions determined by survival value, so that in the end we are driven back to biological agencies summed up in the term natural selection. This argument, however, is based upon what appears to be an erroneous view of the role of selection. Selection is not an originative agent and mind cannot be said to be its product. Very little seems to be known of the ultimate source of variations and this applies to forms of mind as to other things. The mind once arisen is, indeed, limited by biological conditions but it gradually comes to control them by a purposeful handling of the environment and in so doing modifies the conditions of its own survival.

Similar considerations apply to the part played by heredity. In social evolution transmission through tradition takes the place of transmission through the genetic structure. This has many obvious but important consequences. Firstly, it makes cumulative change more intelligible than in biology, where apart from an appeal to the disputed theory of the inheritance of acquired characters, the problem seems intractable. Moreover, inventions or other social changes can be transmitted from one society to another, even though they may be widely separated in space or time—a process to which, I take it, there is no analogy in organic evolution. Next, the process of transmission through diffusion and tradition is not only more intelligible than biological heredity; it is also vastly more rapid and more controllable. Finally, since each generation can start on the basis of what has been acquired by past generations and can, moreover, exercise some choice and selection, it is not surprising that there is some continuity of direction in social evolution. In organic evolution, on the other hand, orthogenesis, or change in what appears as a directed line, must remain a mystery until more is known of the origin of mutations.

NATURAL SELECTION IN SOCIAL EVOLUTION

Of the three main ideas which enter into the theory of evolution, namely variation, heredity, and selection, it is the last that has had the most profound repercussions in its application to human affairs. Suggested originally, as Darwin tells us by Malthus's *Essay on Population*, the formula of the struggle for existence, especially in the more vivid phrase, 'the survival of the fittest' came back to the social study of conditions with the added prestige it had gained as affording an explanation of organic evolution. Darwin himself, it is true, made no extravagant claims for natural selection in the realm of social evolution. He maintained that in the formative period man had acquired his intellectual and moral faculties under the influence of natural selection. But he saw that in later phases the development of these faculties owed much more to training, education and tradition. Generally, in dealing with the 'civilised' nations, Darwin attaches only subordinate importance to natural selection, since 'such nations do not supplant and exterminate one another as do savage tribes'. He adds that 'it is very difficult to say why one civilised nation rises, becomes more powerful and spreads more widely than another; nor why the same nations progress more quickly at one time than another'.[14] The operation of natural selection is only 'tentative'; in actual operation it is affected by many others, including social factors. Thus, for example, he suggests that the decline of ancient Greece may be attributed to friction between its small states, to slavery and, possibly, to extreme sensuality.

THE MISNAMED 'SOCIAL DARWINISM'

Darwin's disciples made no such reservations. In this country there were many who followed Karl Pearson in his view that 'selection is the sole effective process known to science by which a race can continuously progress'.[15] Both here and abroad there arose the movement named by continental writers, with great unfairness to Darwin, 'Social Darwinism'. This movement passed through different phases and it is not easily characterised in general terms. Very often it purported to provide a biological basis for theories of race and class and readily passing from what is or is coming to be to what ought to be it pretended to find in biology an ethical justification for existing inequalities and for condemning all efforts at mitigating struggle within and between groups as an 'interference' with natural laws. In its milder manifestations the ideas underlying Social Darwinism gave rise to the various forms of the Eugenic movement, the main aim of which is to replace natural by rational selection. In its early phases this movement had a strong anti-environmentalist and sometimes a virulent race bias. The horrifying use made by the Nazis of race theories may have contributed to bring about a change of attitude even on the part of those who still favour biological interpretations of social evolution. It may be that the reaction has gone too far, and that we are now passing through a period of extreme environmentalism, in which the study of the influence of selection on the innate constitution of peoples is unduly neglected. In the main, however, it remains that years of controversy have led to the general rejection of the theory that social evolution depends on natural selection, and to the acceptance of the view that the principal factors of social change are social rather than genetic, depending on changes in organisation, knowledge and belief, rather than on changes in the inherited structure, under the influence of selection.

THEORIES RELATING TO RACIAL ADMIXTURE

An interesting survival of the earlier biological theories of social evolution is found in theories attaching importance to the supposed effects of race crossing or race blending on cultural and social change. William McDougall,[16] for example, found in the influence of race crossing an explanation of the advances made by European peoples compared with what he took to be the stagnation of China and India. The main cause of advance he finds indeed in social rather than purely genetic factors. The advance made by European peoples he attributes mainly to the growth of a spirit of inquiry leading to great discoveries in science and technology. But this growth was, in his view, favoured by special conditions which resulted from the repeated fusions and conquests to which the European peoples were subjected. The clash of ideas and beliefs which resulted served to loosen the bonds of custom and religious sanctions. Above all it led to the formation of an aristocracy able to turn its energies to the arts and the knowledge of natural forces. Moreover, since the races entering into the mixture were of allied stocks, crossing did not result in recognisably different offspring, bearing outward marks of inferiority. The stratification that emerged was therefore not caste-like, and there was opportunity for talent to rise from below. In China, McDougall suggests the population was relatively homogeneous in race, and thus lacked the impetus due to race crossing; while in India the racial background was too heterogeneous for stability and progress. These arguments it will be seen are highly speculative, and McDougall offers no suggestions as to how they might be tested or verified. Further, he takes for granted the superiority of the white races in mental qualities, and predicts dire consequences of any fusion with other races. In any case he offers no method for discriminating between the genetic and social effects of race blending. This difficulty applies also to the views of such a writer as J. M. Robertson. A stout antagonist of racial explanations in history, he nevertheless attaches some importance to the blending of stocks as favouring variability.[17] He seems to accept the view that the blending of stocks differing widely in their biological make-up is likely to produce unhappy results. But here again it is difficult to distinguish between the purely biological effects and the effects arising out of disparities in the culture-stage of the races in question. The difficulties which theories of this sort have to meet have not as far as I know been resolved by more recent work on racial admixture. It has to be remembered, that in many instances culture contact results in vast changes where the purely ethnic effects are slight or nil, and that the social or cultural effects are out of all proportion to the degree of admixture.[18] It seems likely, therefore, that even where there is physical admixture the social results—whether favourable or unfavourable—depend more on the nature of the cultures in contact than on the purely biological action of race blending. On the whole question of the racial factor in civilisation, it is clear that we have at present no method for estimating the influence of racial composition on the character and institutions of nations or on the changes they undergo, and it seems safe to conclude that, except perhaps in the case of the most long-standing and deep-seated racial distinctions, race has not been a leading factor in social evolution.

STRUGGLE AND SURVIVAL IN SOCIAL EVOLUTION

The notions of struggle and survival have been applied to ideals, beliefs, institutions. This use of the terms is perhaps most plausible in the case of economic institutions. It makes sense to say that certain crafts die out in the competitive struggle, or that by improvements in technique and organisation certain types prevail and grow in size and power while others dwindle or die out. In these cases the process involved can be observed and studied in detail. In other fields the analogy with the struggle of genetic variants is too slight to be of much help. To say that the fittest beliefs survive is not illuminating, since the fitness is inferred from their survival. In any case there are important differences between the struggle of living organisms and the struggle of ideas, beliefs, etc. For obviously the predominance of ideas or institutions does not depend on the elimination of the persons opposing them, and innovations may survive and be widely adopted even though their originators may have perished.

Finally, a good deal of confusion has arisen from the use of the term 'social selection'. This may be used in a biological sense to describe the influence of social institutions on the genetic make-up of peoples. Thus it is possible, as Galton argued, that the institution of the celibacy of priests may have sensibly affected the distribution of innate ability among the peoples who adopted it. Again a totalitarian regime may drive out the more independent individuals and, so far as mental independence has a genetic basis, produce important changes in the innate constitution of the stock. But there is a form of selection which has nothing to do with the elimination of certain variants or the substitution of one genetic type for another. The quality of the stock remaining constant, society may by its institutions encourage certain elements and discourage others, alter the relative composition of the various classes within it and shape the conditions which determine the type of man that is to be on top, politically, professionally or industrially. The selection thus exercised is of high importance quite apart from the biological consequences, if any such there be, that it may bring with it.

In sum the concepts of variation, inheritance of variations, and selection can with suitable qualifications be usefully employed in interpreting social change. But the agencies involved are different from those operative in organic evolution. Moreover, they are often more intelligible, more easily verifiable, and less open to the kind of difficulties which at present confront biological theory.

SOCIAL DEVELOPMENT AND THE GROWTH OF RATIONALITY

We can now turn to the conception of evolution as meaning not only descent from a common stock, but also a movement in some sense from 'lower' to 'higher' forms—an 'advancement in organization'. This advance is seen most strikingly in the evolution of nervous systems and concomitant mental powers. The higher forms possess sense organs of greater range and sensitivity, accompanied by great sensitivity and subtlety of response and increased capacity for co-ordinating experience. One test of their advance is their increasing independence of environmental contingencies. The process is continued in man, but after the formative period it goes on, not through changes in the organic structure, but through the emergence of a new type of structures, the social structures, themselves the result of inter-actions between men. Human development is to a large extent the development of co-operation. Men learn from one another to an extent unknown in the animal world, and through co-operative activity achieve infinitely greater results than any the individual mind could achieve. The range of co-operation is moreover vastly extended through the emergence of a new form of heredity, transmission through tradition and extra-organic tools. This is not to deny the importance of contributions by exceptional individuals. But even their thought is dependent on the social milieu and the accumulated knowledge of the past. Whether or not the more intelligent animals are also the more social, in man the social factor becomes of decisive importance in the growing power of mind. Mental evolution and social evolution become increasingly connected in the course of the develop-ment of mankind.

From the point of view thus reached the theory of social evolution has obvious links with older theories of human development, especially the earlier theories of progress. There are some features of these earlier theories which are still of interest and importance.

SOCIAL DEVELOPMENT POTENTIALLY WORLD-WIDE

In the first place, for these theories the subject of development was humanity, the entire human race. It is true that the data at their command were derived almost entirely from the history of European civilization, and that they tended to identify the development of humanity with the development of the European peoples or even of the peoples they took to be their elite. Nowadays this would be con-demned as cultural imperialism, and many would regard the notion of humanity as an empty abstraction. Nevertheless, it makes sense to consider the various domains of human achievement, knowledge, law, morals, social organization as contributions to a common stock and as potentially the possession of the whole of mankind. This is clearest in the case of science and its applications. Science is one in the sense that the phases of its growth constitute an intelligible series which can be traced back to the earliest times and to which all peoples have contributed their share. In the spectacular achievements of modern science, the Western peoples have no doubt played a pre-dominant role. Nevertheless, they are but the consummation of a process continuous with the process whereby early man discovered the elementary tools several hundred thousand years ago. It may even be argued that the first steps were the most difficult and the

108

most pregnant. Similarly, though religions are many and morals differ among different peoples, they can nevertheless be regarded as engaged in a common task, as 'experiments in living', which men make in diverse ways to come to terms with themselves and the world.

COMPLEX INFLUENCE OF GROWTH OF KNOWLEDGE

In the second place, I think, the earlier theories were right in emphasising the role played by the growth of knowledge, theoretical and practical, in human development. It is true they claimed too much for intellectual development, and they were mistaken in assuming that truth, virtue and happiness necessarily went together. But if intellectual development is not the sole determinant of progress, it is certainly one of the determining factors, and by no means the least important. I do not see how anyone can doubt the growing importance of reflective and systematic thought in the development of economic and political institutions, of law, morals and religion. All religions develop theologies and are increasingly subject to the modifying influences of knowledge in other fields, whether of natural science or of reflective and self-critical morality. Morals in their turn are subject to rational scrutiny in the light of the growing knowledge of the nature of man and of society. An immense amount of thought goes into the making and reconstruction of legal systems, and in later phases, attempts are made to disentangle the assumptions and underlying principles of the law and to base legislation on some conception of general well-being. The direct influence of the natural sciences and of technology on social life are visible to everyone. The indirect consequences are equally immense. They are often unforeseen and even unforeseeable. But efforts are beginning to be made to subject them to examination and, if possible, to control them. The influence of the growth of knowledge upon social life is more complex and more variable than was envisaged by the earlier theories of progress, but their estimate of its strength remains unshaken, and is, indeed, confirmed by recent developments.

If these considerations are borne in mind, the significance of evolutionary theories in the study of human development will be seen in clearer light. We shall not expect to find parallel stages of culture following each other in regular sequence everywhere. Institutions and other elements of culture embody the efforts of men to adjust their relations to each other and to the world and they have the characteristics not of automatic responses but of purposive striving. As they pass from the early gropings through trial and error to the stages of conscious direction and control societies become increasingly

H

capable of learning from others and adapting what they take from others to their own requirements. Parallel sequences no doubt occur, but as often as not the similarity is merely apparent. Thus, for example, historians of religion have shown that many peoples have passed from a stage of tribal or local deities to a stage of national polytheism and thence to monotheism. But the way in which monotheism was reached by the Hebrews differs radically from the path followed by the Greeks, and the movement towards greater unity need not always culminate in monotheism, but may find expression in some form of pantheism. In this, as in other cases, uniform development is not to be expected and is not, in fact, found.

PROGRESS, PERSISTENCE, AND DECAY

If development is not uniform, neither is it always or necessarily progressive.[19] Here the biological analogy is instructive. For according to recent biological theory, progress, in the sense defined by biologists, is not a common occurrence and is not a law of evolution. The history of life affords many examples of persistence or decay. There are many species which, having reached a certain point, undergo no further development, and many have died out. Indeed according to Julian Huxley there has been progress and there is the possibility of further progress, along one line only—the line of man.[20] It may well be that in social evolution too progressive development is only one of the many forms of developments thrown up, though this may be the one that holds out the greatest promise of further development.

While in some ways the biological analogy is helpful, in others it may be misleading. We cannot expect to arrange the societies of the world in an order of advance. Societies and cultures are not separate organisms. What is a distinguishable unit from the point of view of political structure may be but a fraction of a more inclusive unit considered economically or culturally. Quite apart from the difficulty of demarcating the units to be compared, there are even greater difficulties arising from the vagueness and the complexity of the criteria that have been used in estimating progress. The most that we can hope to attain is some notion of what we mean by levels of development as applied to the main domains of culture, considered as contributions to a common stock belonging to the whole of mankind. How far particular societies satisfy these criteria is another and much more difficult problem. For advance in one direction does not necessarily mean advance in others, and it is obviously very difficult to balance over-all gains and losses.

CONCEPT OF LEVELS OF DEVELOPMENT

What then do we mean by levels of development? In the case of the growth of knowledge the criteria are sufficiently clear. A science for example, is considered as more highly developed in so far as it is internally more consistent, and in so far as it serves to explain phenomena inadequately explained in earlier stages and, in addition, phenomena hitherto unexplained or unknown. In the case of the deductive sciences the criteria are coherence or systematic connectedness. In other sciences the test is the degree to which deductive reasoning can be brought into relation with observation and experiment and the range of experience which can be thus explained. Important elements in the advance of knowledge are the growth of a method of self-criticism and reconstruction and the extent to which underlying assumptions are made explicit.

Is the concept of levels of development applicable to conduct or behaviour? Clearly in so far as conduct consists in the use of means to achieve human ends, the tests of rationality are, at least in part, applicable. There have obviously been enormous advances in technology, and these have depended on increasing insight into the forces of nature and the extent to which the knowledge thus gained has enabled man to use and transform the material supplied by nature. The critical points in this advance have been marked by radical changes in the kind and extent of the knowledge involved. Compare the knowledge indicated by the transition from food-gathering to food producing, or from the use of the overt forces of nature such as wind and water to the discovery of the hidden or underlying forces, systemised in the modern sciences of atomic physics, chemistry and genetics. The criteria of advance in this respect are the same as those that apply to knowledge generally, namely, systematic connectedness and range of application, supplemented by the extent and nature of the control of natural forces which advance in knowledge makes possible.

Does reason penetrate to the ends of action? This will be challenged by those who adopt Hume's view that reason is and ought to be the slave of the passions, that its function is exhausted in serving ends, ultimately not of its making. But this view which seems so plausible is in fact based on an antiquated faculty psychology. The lesson of comparative psychology is that cognition, feeling and conation are in varying degrees intertwined at all stages of behaviour. The basic needs of the organism are laid down in the hereditary structure, but they are transformed by the growth of intelligence and the influence of social factors. As the individual matures he discovers that what

111

he wants and what he needs are not necessarily the same. Analytic reflection is required to discover what it is in the objects we seek that we desire and why it is that we seek satisfaction where it is not to be found. New needs, purposes and ideals are generated with growth of knowledge of human capacities and the opportunities that nature provides for their fulfilment. The individual's tastes and wants are, moreover, shaped and conditioned by social factors. Far from being simply given, the ends of life are complex and variable. They cannot be attributed to feeling or cognition 'in themselves'. There are desires which are only possible at a certain level of cognitive development, and there are thoughts which are only possible at certain levels of emotional intensity.

The blending of knowing, striving, and feeling is especially characteristic of moral ideals. Ideals have a structure which is only slowly discovered. The ideal of bodily and mental health, for example is defined by the biological and psychological sciences, the ideal of truth is defined by logic, that of beauty by aesthetics. The ideals are normative in the sense that they define the conditions which are necessary for their fulfilment, including the control of immediate impulse and the cultivation of qualities of character without which such control is impossible. The norms find intellectual expression in judgments of value or obligation; but without a basis of feeling and impulse these would be without force. As actually operative the conscience is compact of feeling, impulse and cognition. It has, as Butler saw, both power and authority, power in that it can control or induce, though not necessarily completely determine, action; authority in the sense of rational constraint, analogous to the relation in which we stand to all that is or is taken to be objective.

MORAL DEVELOPMENT AS AN ASPECT OF RATIONAL DEVELOPMENT

If these arguments are sound, then the notion of levels of development may be regarded as applicable not only to the knowledge of means but also of ends. In both respects moral development may accordingly be regarded as an aspect of rational development. It has consisted in the growing power of reason to relate the instincts and emotions to general and permanent needs and, with the aid of the imagination, to construct ideals going beyond what is to what might be, if the obstacles to human fulfilment were removed. It is, as Kant saw, in becoming rational that man became moral. This is not to say that intellectual and moral development coincide. Moral codes are affected by the social institutions within which they are embodied and which they only slowly pervade and in varying degrees modify. These may be conceived as experiments in adjusting human relations to the needs of life. But in their earlier stages the experiments are of the nature of trial and error gropings, and changes are not guided by conscious purpose. The rational element gains in strength as men begin to pose the problems of human relations consciously and seek to discover the conditions of progress or deterioration. In the course of this development the ethical element proper, that is the distinctively moral attitude, is differentiated from the other factors shaping human life, such as the religious and the legal. Moral development, on this view, has resulted in the deeper appreciation of human needs and purposes, the clarification of moral ideals and the widening of human sympathies, leading slowly to the recognition that moral principles are universal in scope, applicable to man as man.

If moral development is an aspect of rational development, we should expect that the criteria applicable to the one should be applicable also to the other. This, I think, can be shown to be the case. Moral codes, as I have tried to argue elsewhere[21] may be compared in respect of (i) differentiation, that is the emergence of a distinctively moral attitude, distinguishable in its nature and sanctions from legal and religious rules; (ii) universalisation, the extension of the range of persons to whom moral rules are held to be applicable, a process which seems to involve both a firmer grasp of principle and a widening of the sympathetic impulses and feelings; (iii) systematic connectedness and articulation of underlying principles; (iv) capacity for self-criticism and self-direction, especially the extent to which public policy comes to be shaped by conceptions of well-being and disinterested ascertainment of the relevant facts; (v) comprehensiveness and flexibility, that is the range of needs and interests to which they are responsive, their openness to new values and the way they deal with conflicting claims. It is clear that advance in one direction does not necessarily involve advance in the others. But on the whole the level of moral development depends on the extent to which the various criteria meet. In other words the value of a moral system depends on the coherence and objectivity of the concepts it employs, the extent to which self-critical and reflective thought is allowed and encouraged to pervade conduct in the various spheres of economic and political life, and on the way in which the line is drawn between internal and external sanctions, that is the spheres which are left to the individual and the spheres which are held to call for social control. It is true that the criteria involved emerge into consciousness in the higher societies and that it is they who decide that they are the higher. But this cannot be avoided and is, I believe, what is to be expected, if in fact there has been progress in the evolution of thought and practice.

The criteria I have enumerated are formal. They are tests of rationality in general, applicable to any ends or principles whatever. The question may be raised whether there is any reason for believing that there has been any progress in knowledge of the ends or of the principles of conduct. Some will hold that the ends are constant and that the fundamental principles of morals are simple and have always been known—that we should wish well to others, that hatred is evil, that we should rid ourselves of envy and greed. Others will hold that conceptions of well-being and principles of conduct are indefinitely variable and must always remain so. Neither of these views appears to me acceptable. The constancy of morals is illusory, unless we are to write off the whole history of reflection on human nature and its possibilities as of no significance. Those who believe that the principles of morals are all well known might be invited to try their hands at some of the problems of our own time, for example, the legitimacy and limits of the use of force, and the principles of equitable distribution of the means of life within states and among them. Again there is no doubt that moral codes differ in important respects. But the variations are far from arbitrary, and they do not rule out the possibility that behind the diversity general principles are discoverable which in the course of development come to be recognised as universally binding. The theory of moral evolution implies that such development has in fact occurred, and, in a manner not known in organic evolution, moral development has brought with it convergence and fusion superposed on diversity. Despite appearances to the contrary, I believe, that in modern times there is greater agreement about ends and principles than about the institutions they call for. I am not suggesting that no moral differences remain, but that these are vastly exaggerated as a result of confusions between questions of fact and questions of value, and of the real difficulties involved in applying highly general principles to complex situations and foreseeing the consequences of action in large scale societies.

DEVELOPMENT OF NOTION OF HUMAN RIGHTS

The degree of convergence of moral outlook can be best illustrated perhaps from the history of the notion of human rights. The principle of equality in rights has steadily gained in importance. This is seen in the efforts to reduce or abolish arbitrary differences, such as those based on sex, religion and colour, and secondly, in the extension of the concept of equal rights from the political to the economic, cultural and social spheres. The earlier theories of progress were, I think, right in maintaining that progress consists in a movement towards 'reason and justice' and in considering equality as the core of justice. They did not, however, pay sufficient attention to the difficulties likely to arise out of the complex relations of equality and freedom. The problem of freedom largely arises because either by inborn capacity or as a result of unjust institutions men are unequal in power. Everything that is done to equalise rights should have the effect of equalising power and thus to extend the area of freedom. The difficulty of course is that if power is used to remove hardened inequalities new inequalities are generated which may be even more difficult to remove. There is a similar antinomy whenever coercion is used to promote what is held out to be the ultimate good of those coerced. Examples from our own times are seen in the ruthless use of force to bring about rapid industrialisation in the communist countries on the ground that this will ultimately result in raising the general well-being. In varying degrees of acuteness analogous problems have been involved in the struggle for freedom everywhere in the modern world. Experience shows that while at certain stages the liberation of the individual can only be achieved by a reduction of the power of the state, at others it is through state action that freedom can be won for the individual. In theory it is widely agreed that the ultimate aim is the liberation of the individual and the equalisation of the conditions in which different personalities may have a chance of development. But in practice the problem is complicated by the different ways in which the opposing forces are balanced at different levels of development and especially by the steady increase in the scale of organization. Whether behind the different solutions that have been attempted there are radical differences about ends and principles it is very difficult to decide. But indications of convergence are to be seen in the growing acceptance of the view that the problems involved change in character at different levels of economic and political development and that the answers must vary with the scale of organization, the degree of social differentiation and the presence of active intermediary bodies, standing between the state and the mass of individuals.

DEVELOPMENT OF LEGAL SYSTEMS

When we come to spheres of social development other than those of knowledge and morals significant long range trends are much more difficult to establish. Most of the attempts that have been made to formulate regular stages in the growth of particular institutions such

115

as the family, property, or political organizations are now seen to have been vitiated by the inveterate tendency to assume a single line of evolution. A more profitable line of approach might perhaps be to consider in the first place the general lines of development in the main forms of social regulation, that is the moral, the legal and the religious and their relations to each other. The moral has already been considered. As far as law is concerned, it seems to me that the formal criteria of rationality—systematic connectedness, range of application, articulation of principles and capacity for self criticism—are applicable. Comparative studies have shown that legal systems have passed from a stage of unreflective custom, in which such changes as occur are largely unconscious, to a stage of declaration, systematisation and codification, Thereafter, some societies have passed to a stage of law-making. This may be achieved in some cases, as Maine has shown, by the use of legal fictions, equity and legislation, but no doubt the process differs in different systems according to the weight given to statute law, case law and custom and the techniques available for their interpretation. A still higher development is seen in those societies in which systematic efforts are made to base legislation on some conception of well-being, and to use law as an instrument of social policy. A parallel development may be traced in the efforts made to rationalise legal procedure and to reconstruct legal institutions to make them more conformable to the underlying ethical purposes of the law. I think it is clear that if we are searching not for laws of development, but for the light that history may throw on the possibilities which the development of thought opens out to mankind, we have here striking evidence of growth in self-direction and the rational ordering of life. The degree of unification achieved by law is very impressive. I do not know how many independent legal systems there are, possibly ten or so, and of these the majority are hybrids.[22] The systems derived from Roman law and the common law of England between them have been accepted by rather more than half of mankind. Within some of the systems, e.g. the Commonwealth countries, the United States and the Scandinavian countries, the movement for unification has in modern times achieved a great measure of success. It needs hardly to be said that the obstacles in the way of further unification are formidable. Yet it is a sign of advance that the aim has been explicitly formulated, and seeing that the attempts to unify the law are of quite recent origin and extend over a period of not more than a hundred years, what has so far been gained constitutes no mean achievement.[23] To these gains must be added the growth of a system of international law and of numerous institutions serving international economic and social functions.

DEVELOPMENT OF RELIGION

As regards religion, most historians are agreed in discerning a certain unity behind the diversity, and they point to highly general trends of change which warrant the application to them of the concept of evolution or development. Thus, there has been a movement from local or tribal religions to national polytheisms. Both cosmological and ethical reflection have led through mythology and philosophy to notions of a unitary creative power or first principle. There is a trend towards universalism in morals. Between the eighth and the fifth centuries before the Christian era there emerge religions of redemption or salvation, through which men hope to be freed from the limitations of this world, or more positively, to attain blessedness through union with the godhead. Religions of this sort are universalist in implication. They address themselves to the individual and, as such, transcend distinctions of race or nation. The great religions of today are mostly of this type, though as working creeds they retain large survivals of earlier or more primitive forms.

Perhaps the most significant trend from the point of view of social development in general is the gradual moralisation of religion. Indeed, it is arguable that in so far as there has been progress in the evolution of religion, this has been mainly due to a deepening ethical insight. The relations between religion and morals are, however, very varied and complicated. It would seem that the workings of human justice and human ideas of divine justice sometimes move on parallel lines, at others interact, whilst at other times again they diverge. The spirits of animism and even the gods of polytheism reflect the morality of the blood-feud, and even when they reach the notion of a just god administering justice, the standards do not rise above those current in the group life of the time. The ethical codes of the spiritual religions make higher demands; they set up an ideal of conduct which goes far beyond the requirements of current morality and the practical wisdom of the worldly-wise. In doing so, however, they subordinate ethics to religion. In later developments this relation tends in varying degree to be reversed. Ethics is taken as fundamental and advance in religion is tested by the way in which it satisfies the moral consciousness. These broad generalisations are obviously subject to important qualifications. The influence of religion on morality in a particular direction may be counteracted by others in the opposite direction. Thus the growth of the idea that god sees into the heart of man may have strengthened the tendency to an inward morality as against merely outward conformity. On the other hand, the belief in god as the source of the moral order has been associated with a

117

juridical view of morality, and this has resulted in excessive importance being attached to the external sanctions of reward and punishment. Similarly, the belief in one god, the ruler of the entire universe, may have served to induce in men a sense of their littleness and dependence, and thus have encouraged the notion of equality and brotherhood. On the other hand, monotheistic religions are notoriously intolerant; the greater the deity, it seems, the greater the danger to those who do not acknowledge his authority. Again as has frequently been pointed out, the acknowledgement of one god to whom all owe allegiance, does not seem to have done anything to mitigate international animosities. The analysis of the historical facts in matters such as these presents great difficulties. I doubt whether there are any reliable methods for ascertaining whether a decline in religious piety leads to a lowering of the sense of civic duty, or conversely, whether a strengthening of religious faith reacts favourably on the moral consciousness. How, for example, would one test the assertion confidently made by William McDougall that without the belief in reward and punishment in after life, 'nations could not rise to an austere morality or even maintain a decent standard of life'?[24]

DIFFERENTIATION OF LAW, MORALS, AND RELIGION

Returning now to the concept of levels of social development, I should like to lay stress in particular on the criterion of differentiation. This has generally been discussed in reference to the division of labour, a process of great importance in the history of mankind. But equally important is the differentiation of the forms of social control. The level of social development depends, I think, on the level of knowledge and its applications in the control and use of the forces of nature and on the way in which morality, religion and law (including political organisation) are related to each other. In the more developed societies morality tends to become more autonomous, that is, to depend on the inward sanctions of free acceptance. This brings home the necessity of defining the spheres of acts whose value depends on their being freely performed and those which cannot safely be left to individual choice. In other words, it forces into the open the question of the relation between law and morals. In dealing with it there is a real divergence between authoritarian and democratic societies. In the latter it is, I think, true to say that while the law is increasingly moralised in the sense that it is increasingly sensitive to moral opinion, there is at the same time a tendency to reserve certain areas of activity as beyond the scope of legal compulsion or external standardisation. In other words, a distinction comes to be drawn between

118

spheres of action which both require and permit of legal sanctions and others, notably in the areas of self-development and self-expression, which are best left to individual choice and initiative. In authoritarian regimes, on the other hand, public opinion is given little opportunity of systematic expression. At the same time the claim is made that the distination between the law and morals has been overcome; in other words, that the law has been completely moralised. From the point of view of democratic societies this is not a step forward but backward. For in attempting to regulate every detail of life juridically, the distinction between inward and outward sanctions is blurred and this, by diminishing the area of individual choice, cannot but be inimical to the full growth of the moral consciousness.

Equally important in the process by which law, morals and religion have been differentiated is the secularisation of law and politics. This has contributed to the growth of civilisation by removing from the category of criminal and punishable actions matters of belief, such as atheism, heresy and schism, or the non-performance of religious rites, as well as, for example, certain sexual offences. Above all, the importance of secularisation is seen in the separation of spiritual and temporal powers. In European history this separation was a necessary condition of the revival of free inquiry and the spirit of tolerance. The process of secularisation is now going on in many parts of the world, and may have similar consequences. On the other hand some communist countries are reverting to the fusion of spiritual and temporal power in a new form by subjecting art and science to political control. In the long run this must tend to lower the level of social development.

ECONOMIC DEVELOPMENT AND SOCIAL CONTROL

The question may be raised whether the criteria of development so far discussed are applicable to economic growth. Economists, in their anxiety to avoid value judgments, estimate growth by the level of real income and capital per head of the population and by the level of technical achievement. When, however, they discuss policy, value judgments are unavoidable; there has to be a reference to some conception of well-being or of justice, implicit or explicit. From the point of view here adopted, namely that of a rational ethic, it seems to me that economic development, in the sense of advance from lower to higher levels, can be estimated by reference to (i) the nature of the ends which the economic system is taken to serve and the clarity with which these ends are formulated; (ii) the efficiency of the system,

119

the extent to which it succeeds in attaining these ends; (iii) the type of control employed in regulating the social relations of those engaged in economic activities.

As to the ends, I think that in advanced societies it is coming to be more or less explicitly recognised that the function of economic activity in so far as it comes under social control is or ought to be to supply the material conditions of well-being. From this point of view production has to be considered closely in relation to consumption and the problem of distributive justice has to be faced. There are no doubt differences of opinion as to what constitutes well-being. But at the stage of reflection about the ends and principles of conduct reached in advance societies, there is considerable convergence of views, at any rate in regard to minimal requirements. There are greater differences of opinion about the methods or means to be employed than about the ends and principles themselves. Hence the importance of the attempts to estimate efficiency.

Efficiency, of course is relative to ends, but given the ends, its further definition is primarily a matter for the economist. It is for economics to determine the conditions of advance in relation to the resources available or procurable; the optimum distribution of capital and labour in the various sectors of the economy; the scale and pace of industrialisation; the proportion of the national income to be alloted to capital outlay or to investment for consumption; the provision to be made for the education and training of personnel, etc. Presumably the level of advance depends on the way these problems are met and the success of the methods adopted in relation to the ends aimed at. Reference to ends, of course, involves qualitative judgments, and these may present great difficulties. But even gross comparisons such as those based on the distribution of income per head and the use of indices of health and education for the bulk of the population are helpful at least in determining the minimal conditions of well-being, and these can be improved as more accurate methods of ascertainment become available. It must be admitted that opinions differ widely about the principles of equitable distribution. Economists of the classical tradtion were agreed that equality was in itself desirable, but they refrained from advocating any radical changes tending towards equalisation on the ground that such changes by weakening incentives, would be likely to diminish the total available for distribution. It is arguable that conclusions of this sort, while possibly valid for certain levels of economic development, are not valid for all; that for example, given modern technology and productivity, a wider diffusion of the means of well-being is not only compatible with but a condition of economic progress.

In considering types of organization most conducive to economic advance, questions both of fact and of value are involved about which opinion is sharply divided. Many economists believe that the best type of organisation is that which offers the greatest freedom of choice both to producers and consumers. In this they are in harmony with the modern emphasis on the values of spontaneity, individual initiative and responsibility. On the other hand, in emphasising freedom, they fail to do justice to equality. For it cannot be denied that where great inequalities persist, only the few have freedom of choice, and that to extend the range of freedom it may be necessary to limit the freedom of those who have the power to dominate others. If it be agreed that an ultimate aim is to equalize freedom, the questions of methods remain. At this point the idea of levels of development may prove very helpful. The distinction between services best performed by individuals acting independently or by voluntary agreement, and services technically social in the sense that they depend on the use of collective resources and may require legal regulation involving compulsion, depends on the stage of development. The scope and limits of state action in the field of economic organisation cannot be laid down in general terms valid for all time and conditions. What the state can do and ought to do in countries with a highly differentiated social structure, and an active public opinion capable of initiating movements for peaceful change and offering resistance to monopolistic powers, must obviously be very different from what the state can and ought to do in dealing with a population inert politically and not sufficiently diversified to secure diffusion of power. The aim at all times should be to avoid undue concentration of power; the means must obviously vary with the level of differentiation and the strength of the groups or classes competing for power. From the ethical point of view, the level of social development can perhaps be best judged from the scope and the kinds of restraints that a society imposes on its members and the area which it leaves to individual choice—that is, broadly, by the way the line is drawn between the spheres of law and morals. From the economic point of view, the ethical standards have to be viewed in relation to efficiency, or the power to maintain and, where possible, to raise the standard of living.

In sum, on the view here taken, progress in social development is to be judged mainly by the stage reached in the growth of knowledge of nature and of insight into human needs, values and potentialities, and by the extent to which this knowledge and insight are used in the direction of human affairs. To this the objection will no doubt be made that, like the earlier theories of progress, it attaches too much importance to intellectual factors. In regard to moral development, in particular, we shall be asked whether, in view of the advances made in thought, we ought not to expect greater improvements in institutions than we actually find, and how we are to account for the obvious failure to benefit from such knowledge and wisdom as now exist.

POSSIBILITIES OF FURTHER PROGRESS

In dealing with these questions we need not commit ourselves to a doctrine of the indefinite perfectibility of man or of ineradicable original sin. What the facts suggest is that though progress consists in the rationalisation and moralisation of man, the process is still in its early stages. There will be many who would agree with the dictum uttered by Hobhouse in one of his pessimistic moods that if mankind be considered as a whole and compared with an individual organism, 'its hitherto acquired powers of assimilating the teachings of experience must be placed somewhere on the level of the sea anemone'.[25] Among the advanced peoples there is of course a vast stock of knowledge, but this, needless to say, is very unequally diffused, and where it exists is often highly specialised. For the most part behaviour is dominated by habits formed during ages of slow change, and ill-adapted to the intricacies and complexities of modern urban life. That the thing works at all and on an ever-increasing scale is truly astonishing. The failures of reason are palpable enough, but they should not blind us to the successes or shake our belief in the possibilities of further progress.

The problem of behaviour contrary to reason is, of course, not a new one. As far as the individual is concerned the main outlines of a psychological analysis were indeed given by Aristotle in his discussion of the 'incontinent' man, that is the man who knows what is good and does what is bad. As he explains, knowledge of principles in matters of conduct is not enough. The knowledge has to be integrated into the character, and indeed, full knowledge is only possible for the fully formed character. Even when principles are consciously accepted as binding, the application to particular cases may easily go astray. Under the influence of passion or self-interest it is easy to be convinced that the principle prima facie relevant does not apply in our own case, or that the situation is complex and contains elements to which other principles apply. In other circumstances, again, we may, under the sway of deep feelings, begin to wonder whether a principle to which we had hitherto adhered can be true. As Aristotle put it, either the wrong minor premise or the wrong major premise may be adopted in the 'practical syllogism', with the result that conclusions more congruent with our desires are drawn. The resources of self-deception or sophistication are well-nigh endless, as moralists and novelists have repeatedly shown. Modern psychology has deepened these ancient explanations by laying stress on the importance of unconscious factors. Firstly, it has brought out the strength of unconsciousness and repressed instinctive drives and their imperviousness to the influence of reason. Secondly, it has enriched our insight into the distortions to which the conscience is subject and the infinitely varied ways in which the process may be concealed from the agent himself. Thirdly, it has shown, mainly by analysis of certain types of criminal actions, how in various ways cognition and emotion may be dissociated, producing a sort of apathy which robs knowledge of its power to influence action.

In dealing with collective action, it has to be remembered that while there are certain resemblances between individual and collective mentality, there are also important differences. To begin with, a community, such as a nation, can be compared with an individual in so far as it acts as a unit in relation to other similar units. As such it is capable of generous and unselfish acts, but, needless to say, it is only too easily apt to develop a collective egoism, which is all the stronger because of the elements of loyalty and devotion to which it can appeal among its own members. Nations like individuals are guided by self-interest, more or less enlightened, but they can be led by collective pride and self-assertion to act in a manner not only injurious to others, but palpably against their own interests. So far the resemblance to individuals holds. But it has to be remembered that the community as such has no central mind or unitary will. The rationality of its collective action must depend on the rationality of those who act on its behalf and their relation to the individuals or groups composing the community. In autocracies, for example, the degree of rationality must depend mainly on the mentality of those in possession of power. But even they must be influenced by the nature of the tie that binds the people to them and the diffusion of intelligence and political interest among them.

In democracies public opinion has in varying degrees to be satisfied. Those who are entrusted with the shaping of policy have not only to interpret the general will as in a sense to create it. Too often they succeed in neither. Perhaps too much is expected of representative systems. Elections, as Hobhouse reminded us, are not competitive examinations in moral wisdom. It is not surprising, in view of the methods of selection, that representative assemblies often fail in their function of consolidating public judgment and supervising administration in the interest of the common well-being.

Next, whether or not large communities can be correctly said to have a general will, they certainly contain sectional or group wills. These vary greatly in the knowledge at their command and in their regard for the public interest. They may, in working for their own ends, contribute to the formation of a wider social purpose, and, given tolerant interchange, diversity is of itself of value as a condition of free initiative and a protection against undue concentration of power. On the other hand, they have a collective egoism of their own. By various processes of self-deception and rationalisation analogous to those described above, they tend to identify their own interest with the interests of the whole and to enlist the social sentiments attaching to the whole in the service of the part. This is not to say that the exploitation of social sentiments is consciously contrived. It is easy for those engaged in the process to believe what they want others to believe. There seem to be virtually no limits to the confusions and distortions to which the public mind may thus be exposed.

The very highest ideals may be made to play a part in this process of distortion or confusion. Couched in lofty terms, ideals are apt to give a glow of satisfaction without inducing action; instead of inspiring effort they may serve rather as an asylum of escape from effort. They tend to be kept in the safe atmosphere of moral abstractions, not to be taken seriously by practical men, or else to be used to provide spiritual boost for policies which, stated nakedly, would make no appeal. Their failure when put to the test is very readily exploited by the 'realists'. Examples will easily suggest themselves to anyone who considers the use made of ideals of justice, of 'making the world safe for democracy', etc., during the first World War, or the mixture of power politics and moralism in the period following the second World War.

Despite all this it remains that the irrationality of collective action is vastly exaggerated by the pessimists of our day. All are not equal in sin. Public opinion is sometimes enlightened, and on occasions makes itself felt, at least in some communities. The mistakes of statesmen are not always the effects of pressure by sinister interests or of unconscious drives, but may result from genuine difficulties which the wisest and best informed might not be able to resolve. Are the irrationalities really surprising in a world in which social change is still largely shaped by the dead hand of the past and the clash of wills in innumerable, more or less independent centres? The impressive thing is rather that out of the blindness and mutual frustration common needs do come to be recognised, leading slowly to the formation of a common purpose or common purposes.

CONCLUSIONS

I must now try to bring together the main threads of my argument. The principle conclusions which suggest themselves are as follows:

(a) Human evolution is continuous with animal evolution as regards both body and mind.

(b) Mental evolution in man differs radically from mental evolution in the animal world in the part played by social factors, i.e. interactions between minds. This interaction vastly extends the powers of mind, not only directly but indirectly, by enabling its products or achievements to contribute towards further achievements.

(c) Progress in human evolution consists in the growth of rationality, that is, the systematic organisation of thought and experience.

(d) The concept of rationality applies to action as well as to thought. The criteria of advance are substantially the same for both spheres.

(e) The organisation of action consists partly in the use made of the knowledge of nature to serve human ends, and partly in disclosing the nature of these ends and the construction of ideal ends. Whether the advance makes for social progress depends not only on the growth of knowledge and of moral insight, but on the extent to which such knowledge and insight are embodied in social institutions, and through them shape behaviour and mould character.

(f) Development is very uneven in different spheres of thought and action. Thus, advance in ethical ideals may leave religion for long unaffected, and scientific discoveries may not be accompanied by changes in moral or religious outlook. The evolution of the social structure, the evolution of scientific thought and the evolution of religion or of morals follow their own course and have their own history. Their relations to each other are very variable and complex. They differ in their rate of change, the readiness to which advances can be transmitted or diffused from one centre to another, and in their liability to retrogression. Hence the difficulties of prediction. In the later phases, however, the various developments tend to converge, and as the connections between them come to be better understood, conscious efforts towards their harmonization become possible. There may well be critical points beyond which advance will be more continuous and assured.

I

(g) Though no laws of social development or of progress have been established some long-range trends can be discerned which show progress along certain lines and establish the possibility of further progress. In estimating future possibilities the most important trends to be taken into consideration seem to me to be the steady increase in the scale of organisation and the growing interdependence of peoples. Self-contained development even on the part of the largest communities is rapidly becoming more difficult and precarious. While this makes further extension of organisation more urgent, it infinitely complicates the problem of reconciling order with freedom. Both sociological analysis and historical surveys suggest that efficient control of the forces of external nature and of the inner nature of man must rest upon an organisation covering the whole world and must rely on methods which can call forth the willing response of all its members in the service of ends they can recognise as common. At this point ethics and sociology teach the same lesson, and the recognition that a world order based on freedom is both ethically imperative and sociologically possible may prove to be one of the conditions necessary for the attainment of this ideal.

REFERENCES

1. W. E. Heitland, *Behind and Before*, Cambridge, 1924, p. 97.
2. L. Lévy-Bruhl, *La mentalité primitive*. Herbert Spencer Lecture, 1931, Oxford.
3. *The Origin of Species*, World's Classics edition of 1951, p. 559.
4. Various authors, *Evolution in the Light of Modern Knowledge*, New York and London, 1925, p. 334.
5. *Origin*, p. 127.
6. *Evolution as a Process*, London, 1954, p. 11.
7. *Darwin and Modern Science*, ed. A. C. Seward, Cambridge, 1909.
8. A. Meillet & Marcel Cohen, *Les langues du monde*, Paris, 1924. W. Schmidt, *Die Sprachfamilien und Sprachenkreise der Erde*, Heidelberg, 1926.
9. Cf. Gordon Childe, *Progress and Archaeology*, London, 1944, and Edward B. Tylor, *Researches into the Early History of Mankind*, London, 1870.
10. Ibid., p. 374.
11. *Primitive Culture*, London, 1871.
12. T. H. and Julian Huxley, *Evolution and Ethics, 1893-1943*, London, 1947, p. 55.
13. *Origin*, p. 12.
14. *Descent*, p. 216.
15. *Groundwork of Eugenics*, London, 1909, p. 20.
16. Cf. *The Group Mind*, Part III.
17. Cf. *Evolution of States*, London, 1912, p. 63.
18. For examples, see my essay on the Concept of Evolution, in *The Diversity of Morals*, Ch. XI.

126

19. Both these points were clearly seen by the early evolutionists. Cf. F. B. Jevons, *An Introduction to the Study of Religion*, London, 1896.
20. British Association Reports, 1936, 81-100.
21. Cf. *Reason and Experience in Ethics*, London, 1956.
22. Cf. J. H. Wigmore, *A Panorama of the World's Legal Systems*, Washington, 1936.
23. Cf. H. C. Gutteridge, *Comparative Law*, Cambridge, 1946, Ch. XI-XIII.
24. *Body and Mind*, London, 1911, Preface.
25. *Social Development*, London, 1924, p. 336.

B. FARRINGTON

Social Mind and Animal Brain

If we consider two lively subjects of research at the present day, conditioned reflexes and communications, would it be unfair to suggest that underlying the arguments of many able physiologists and cyberneticists is the assumption that the stimulation of the sense organs in man is followed automatically by the formation of thoughts in the brain? That the brain is an organ biologically evolved in such a way as to turn sensations into concepts? More than once I have heard a physiologist follow his demonstration of the capacity of a decerebrated octopus to 'learn' under the stimulus of electric shocks by confident explanations of the human consciousness and the human conscience as systems of conditioned reflexes. If one should seek to remind him of some of Professor Ginsberg's propositions—as, for instance, that 'the basic needs of the human organism laid down in the hereditary structure are transformed by the growth of intelligence and the influence of social factors'; that 'far from being simply given the ends of life are complex and variable'; and that 'there are desires which are only possible at certain levels of cognitive development and thoughts which are only possible at certain levels of emotional intensity'—if one should venture to urge such considerations as these one would run the risk of being dismissed as 'medieval'.

Then there are the cyberneticists. In a recent inaugural at a British university the new professor said: 'Without any further progress in our understanding of the functions of the brain it is certainly possible to aid thought by machines of various kinds. It may even be posssible to build machines that think. I am of the opinion that if such terms as deduction, induction, and so on are defined unambiguously and in a finite number of terms then, in principle, a machine can be designed to carry them out.' To the 'medieval' mind it would seem clear that machines do not think, that they operate not with logical or mathe-

129

B. Farrington

matical concepts but only with physical representations of them. But such distinctions have lost their validity in some high places. Did not the Massachussets Institute of Technology in July 1957 offer a course of lectures on The Psychology of the Man-made Machine? Does not a mass of similar technozoistic phraseology disfigure the pages of many technological and scientific journals? Might not technozoism, like astrology for so many hundreds of years, develop into a sophisticated scientific illusion?[1]

The transition from animal to human mentality is difficult to understand because it involves the contradictory notions of continuity and radical novelty. It is such radical novelties as consciousness and conscience that are ignored by the reductionism of the technozoists. To help us over this stile we might invoke the concept of levels, which has still, I think, a role to play in philosophy. Thirty years ago, in a brilliant and perhaps too soon forgotten book[2] J. S. Haldane arranged the sciences in a series according to their degree of abstraction, the progression being from mathematics, the most abstract, through mechanics, physics, chemistry, biology, to psychology, whose subject-matter he held to be the most concrete and real of all. Haldane was concerned with the existence of levels not only in the sciences but also in nature. For the irreducibility of the sciences from a higher to a lower level is proof of the existence of objective levels in nature; and it is perhaps worth stressing that the psychic world, the last to be evolved, is not for that reason the less real. It would seem that a more complex organisation of matter is accompanied by the emergence of a cluster of new and unique qualities, with the result that every set of natural laws has a limited validity. Yet the levels are not completely distinct from one another. The more complex can only arise out of the less complex, even though the emergence of new qualities is not strictly predictable and therefore not reducible to causality. On the other hand—a point of great importance—the higher levels, once they have emerged, act, or may act, upon the lower. For this reason, although the psychic world, with its economic, social, and cultural levels, has emerged out of the physical and biological world, there is no reason why it should not be regarded as a natural force and potentially the greatest of all forces in nature with power to modify and control its physical and biological environment.[3]

The foregoing argument is intended to suggest the impropriety of regarding the evolution of society as dependent on biological causes. Here it is relevant to recall, as Professor Ginsberg has not failed to remind us, that evolution as a social theory is older than Darwinism. Before Darwin was born Sir William Jones had accounted for the similarities of structure in certain languages by the hypothesis of their

130

descent from a common ancestor. Like Darwin's, his theory also set aside a Biblical myth, yet it was readily accepted and has proved a fertile instrument of research. Nobody in possession of the evidence doubts it. The ease of its acceptance would seem to be due to the completeness with which the case for it was made out. In this it contrasts with Darwinism, the social implications of which, naturally enough since it is a biological theory, are far from being agreed by all.

THE SOCIAL CHARACTER OF KNOWLEDGE

Professor Ginsberg has distinguished with fullness of information and nicety of judgment the respective spheres of biological and social theory, and I am reminded in this connection of the penetrating observation of one of the pioneers of social evolutionary theory. About seventy years before Sir William Jones found the clue to the history of the Indo-Germanic family of languages Vico[4] had given the first hint of the evolutionary view of human society that was to dominate his *New Science*. His standpoint was that it is easier for man to understand the development of *society*, because he has himself made it, than to penetrate the mysteries of *nature*, which are known only to their Maker. Significantly the first use he made of his social theory was to aim a side-thrust at the natural philosophy of Descartes. He suggested that our complete comprehension of geometrical demonstrations results from the fact that geometry is a social construct. The general drift of his developed theory was to suggest that the human mind has a social history. Earlier enquirers into the rise of human institutions lacked this insight. They found the remote beginnings of religion and politics incomprehensible because they lacked the key to the phases of man's mental development. Vico, bringing to the study of jurisprudence unique powers of historical imagination, perceived—and the new insight struck him with the force of a revelation—that man as he emerged from the forest to a hut-dwelling, from the hut to the village, from the village to the town, from the town to the city with its academies and universities, passed also through a mental evolution which accorded with the stages of his social progress. It is, I think, true and, if true, unfortunate, that Vico's criticism of Descartes has had too little attention. And even before Vico, Descartes' contemporary, Gassendi, had protested to him that by ignoring the socio-historical conditioning of the mind, Descartes was committing a major blunder. To the propounder of the philosophy of *cogito ergo sum* he writes in a letter: 'You will say, "I am mind alone" . . . But let us talk in earnest, and tell me sincerely, Do you not derive the very sounds you utter in so saying from the

B. Farrington

society in which you have lived? And since the sounds you utter are derived from intercourse with other men, are not the meanings of these sounds derived from the same source?'[5]

This awareness of the social character of knowledge has been making, and losing, its way down the centuries. If Gassendi in the seventeenth century had so firm a grasp of it, he probably owed it to his mastery of Epicureanism. But when it is forgotten sociology suffers. One period of such forgetfulness came with the success of the Darwinian theory of biological evolution. It is notorious that such fine sociologists as Herbert Spencer, E. B. Tylor, and J. G. Frazer were prone to ascribe to biological processes phenomena that demand sociological analysis. In spite of his vastly greater accumulation of material the scientific character of Frazer's work, if I may hazard such a judgment, is on a lower level than that of his short-lived predecessor, Robertson Smith. Nor is it without significance that Robertson Smith acknowledged a deep debt to the seventeenth-century founder of comparative religion, John Spencer. In the study of society any impairment of historical sense is a disaster which can certainly not be compensated by acquaintance with the natural sciences. Gordon Childe's judgment on Tylor and Frazer was that they 'had succeeded in draining rituals and beliefs of all that was vital to the societies that practised and entertained them'.[6]

In the investigation of the sociology of knowledge I think nobody of my generation in the English-speaking world did better work than Gordon Childe. He, of course, accepted the doctrine of organic evolution and with it the continuity between natural and human history. The establishment of that continuity is the great, the epoch-making, gift that biology has made to sociology. But to the end of his life, and progressively as his mastery of his subject deepened, Childe gave warning that without stringent precautions 'the application of evolutionary terms and concepts to human history may do more harm than good'. His main point was that 'the intrusion of diffusion as an agent of evolution . . . has so drastically altered the historical process that no analogy between the evolution of species and the evolution of societies is valid'. In short, as he puts it, in human society 'random mutations are replaced by discoveries and inventions' and these 'are transmitted not by copulation but by education'.[7] Here again it may be recalled that it was Francis Bacon in the seventeenth century who, out of the depth of his knowledge of the history of human society, placed the revolutionary role of inventions and discoveries on its unassailable foundation.

Nevertheless, though often misleading or supererogatory, analogies between biological and social evolution remain seductive because

132

they appeal to a long-established pattern of human thought. The belief in astrological influences dominated the European mind throughout most of its intellectual history and has only just sunk below the horizon, its afterglow being still plainly visible in the western sky. This was followed by a reliance, equally erroneous, on terrestrial influences, the belief that the climate, the soil, the geology, the flora, the fauna, the physical configuration of the various regions of the earth, determine the history of their human populations. Against this geographical determinism the school of human geography founded by Vidal de la Blache has, in the last few decades, waged a magnificent fight. The contention of this school might be summed up in the following way. For the concept of *influences* exerted by the earth on man, a concept which lacks all scientific basis and reduces man to passivity, should be substituted the concept of *relations* between man and his natural habitat, which not only gives a basis for scientific research but restores to man his dignity as an active agent.[8] Now it is undeniable that there has existed a tendency to let biological determinism succeed to the role of astrological and geographical fatalism. The revolt against this tendency, as was the case with the revolt against astrological causality by Pico della Mirandola and others, should be both scientific and moral. It offends both the reason and the conscience; and in this sphere also we need to substitute for the concept of the *influence* upon man of his animal nature the truer concept of the *relations* between man and his animal inheritance.

Let us consider, in the case of one fundamental human institution, what this change of concepts involves. We meet again and again the phrase 'the natural family' employed in a context which implies that this fundamental institution of human society is a purely biological phenomenon. But this is not so. A Roman father whose wife bore him a child would not have thanked you for describing this biological event as 'an addition to his family'. That was for him to decide. It was for him *quod natum est tollere*—a phrase which distinguishes neatly the part played by nature and the part played by society in the institution of the family. There really is no such thing in the history of human society as the natural family. However far back you go what you do find is an institution, a social convention, established for dealing with a natural event by a collective human force acting through constituted authority. The same holds true of even more elementary facts. Neither the wearing of clothes nor going naked, neither eating nor defecation, is for man a purely natural act. Some social convention will regulate its performance. Man is a social being, and the function of society is to control nature.

What conclusion results from these considerations? I accept the

133

view that anatomically, physiologically, and even psychologically there is continuity between the evolution of animals and men. That is to say, the *brain* of man is the end product of biological evolution. But the *mind* of man is another thing, and sociologists operate wholly within the domain of mind. To quote Durkheim: 'Sociology places itself from the start in the ideal sphere; it does not arrive there by slow degrees, as the end of its researches; it sets out from there. The ideal is its proper domain'.[9] Or as Ginsberg puts it more briefly: 'Mental development in man is a social process'.[10]

Let us pause a little longer on this topic of the social aspect of human consciousness. Here I take the opportunity to acknowledge a debt to a French sociologist, the late Jean Przyluski. He is the author of a series of books, *Participation, L'Evolution Humaine, Créer*, the attraction of which for myself I might suggest in this way. Many years ago, wrestling with Hegel's *Phenomenology of the Spirit*, a work in which vast ideas move but move as in a fog, I thought: if only a Frenchman would write a history of the progress of the human spirit through history, and do so with Gallic lucidity and grace, what a prize that would be! In Przyluski's trilogy I found something more like this than I had dared to hope. Permit me, then, to clarify the concept of the collective aspect of human mentality by some of his formulations. 'A theory of knowledge,' he writes, 'cannot be exclusively psychological; it must be founded on a broader basis, because knowledge is a psycho-social reality.' Again he says: 'It is only in the activity of certain individuals, savants, artists, philosophers, mystics, that the results of personal experience play a preponderating role.' And, lest we should misunderstand that word *preponderating*, he adds: 'Knowledge is collective for the most part; if it be individual in a certain measure, yet it is always collective in its foundations and in most of the elements which compose it'.[11]

LANGUAGE AND MAN'S SECOND NATURE

Of this collective knowledge, which is the distinctive possession of man, speech is the medium. Now in regard of the emergence of human speech it seems to me right to recognize here the activity and creativity of man. Speech is not something that happened to man, but something he did. It is the act which made him man. This is what is implied in the denial of any phylogenetic connection between the animal brain and the mind of man. Invoking the concept of levels, we should regard the brain of the hominid as the necessary natural basis for the development of mind; the mind we should regard as a novel, unpredictable, emergent phenomenon, connoting a new kind of activity on the part of the being which then came into existence. The essence of the transformation was the passage from blind instinct to conscious purpose. The process doubtless extended over many millennia, but logically it is a single act.

In the analysis of the origin and nature of human speech we find again a divergence between the biological and sociological view. In these two views there may be agreement that the instinctive, expressive, hereditary cries of animals are radically different from the conceptual, communicative, acquired speech of men. Nevertheless the attempts of Keith and Elliot Smith to establish the linguistic capacity of extinct human types on the evidence of skull structure are examples of the impropriety of seeking an anatomical solution for a cultural problem. A similar misconception underlay the endeavour of another biologist to teach an orang-outang to say 'papa'. Some progress was noticed in the course of six months, but the gratified teacher was not entitled to claim that he had thrown any light on the origin of human speech. The linguist finds such an investigation wrong in principle.[12] There is no phylogenetic connection between animal cries and human speech, which are only superficially the same kind of phenomenon, animal cries being without conscious communicative intent. Révész, indeed, points out that the distinctive character of human speech was clearer some two hundred years ago to men such as Vico, Buffon, and Herder than it has been to some twentieth-century enquirers. Perhaps one of the main values of the new study of the history of ideas is that it reminds us of the power of brilliant new discoveries, such as those of conditioned reflexes and the principle of the negative feed-back, to induce forgetfulness of older truths. The old humanistic ideal of education as *cognitio cogniti* has lost none of its value.

Ancient Greek and Roman speech distinguished by separate words the world of nature from the world of man. Cicero drew out the implication of this popular distinction in an admirable formula. He concludes a magnificent hymn to creative labour with these words: 'Thus, by the use of our own hands, we bring into being within the realm of Nature a second nature for ourselves'.[13] This formulation we all accept as one of the fundamental categories of our thought.

Of this man-made world speech is, from the beginning, a necessary pre-condition. Professor Hogben has discerned the uniqueness of man in the fact that he is talkative, tool-making, and supremely teachable; and we should recognise that standardised tools could not be made by an animal without the capacity of conceptual speech. Rudimentary speech, we may suppose, was never divorced from action but existed as an accompaniment and supplement of the

135

religious and industrial life, from which function it gradually derived its conceptual character, since it was a schematisation in word and gesture of the ritual and industrial activities. Thus modern linguistic theory no longer finds it adequate to describe language as a means of communication. 'Language', writes Collingwood, 'is not a device whereby knowledge already existing is communicated, but an activity, prior to knowledge itself, without which knowledge could never come into existence.'[14] Ernst Cassirer makes the same point: 'According to traditional teachings of logic', he writes, 'the mind forms concepts by taking a certain number of objects which have common properties . . . and abstracting from their differences. . . . But how can such *differentiae* exist prior to language? Do we not rather realise them only by means of language, through the very act of naming them? . . . Before the intellectual work of conceiving and understanding phenomena can begin, the work of *naming* must have preceded it, and have reached a certain point of elaboration. For it is this process which transforms the world of sense impressions, which animals also possess, into a mental world, a world of ideas and meanings.' 'Thus the special symbolic forms are not imitations but *organs* of reality, since it is solely by their agency that anything real becomes an object for intellectual apprehension.'[15]

From this analysis of language, as not merely a reflection of external reality but an agent in our intellectual apprehension of it, a new doctrine of relativity emerges. We all, as I have said, accept Cicero's notion of a second nature within the realm of Nature, which man has made for himself to dwell in. We have not always perceived the epistemological significance of this fact. For this second nature is not merely, or even primarily, a material world but a mental one. As such this second man-made nature is the instrument by which man observes and acts upon external nature. The sense-perceptions in man function in a specific way because he is a speaking animal. The collective world-picture which every infant learns to construct from the impressions on his sense-organs is conditioned by the conceptual framework given to him as he learns to speak. This framework comprises all the categories of consciousness. Concepts of space and time, quantity and quality, natural and artificial, holy and profane, thing and person, substance and event, cause and effect, organic and inorganic, work and play, no less than all the institutions, arts, and sciences, which depend upon these distinctions being made—all these are mental artefacts with no very ancient history. That history is hardly older than *homo sapiens*. Perhaps its effective beginning is not older than the oldest cave-paintings of which we have knowledge, although I have no wish to rob palaeolithic man of his contribution to the early stages of the intellectual pre-history of man. No doubt the *praeparatio linguistica* of man filled many hundreds of millennia.

Now this mental world created so recently by society is the instrument by which man observes and analyses nature. Physicists have lately become acutely conscious of the disturbances produced by the instruments and processes of observation in the phenomena observed. We should recognise an even vaster effect on the whole of our knowledge of nature produced by the consciousness of the observers. Nature, as we know it, is not an objective reality conveyed by our senses into our minds but a construct made out of a very limited range of sense impressions by a mentality which is itself a social product in a continuous and fairly rapid state of development. It is for this reason, as it seems to me, that all science divorced from philosophy is dangerously misleading. As scientists we should be nothing but grateful to a philosopher like Hannah Arendt who not only invites us to stop and think what we are doing but helps us to do so.[16]

There is a great practical distinction between the biological and the sociological or philosophical theory of man. The biological theory of evolution reveals man as the passive product of blind natural forces. The study of man in society, however, is concerned with man not as he is pushed on from behind by the law of cause and effect, but as as he is pulled on from in front by the idea he forms of what his future might be. 'The anticipation of the future', says Przyluski, 'has no less importance than the knowledge of the past. We interpret the past in the light of the present and of the future. The actual is without significance except in relation to the virtual, to the possible, to the future; and the progress of evolution is dependent on our will, because it is only human freedom that can actualise the virtual, the possible, the future.'[17]

In our troubled times we often hear it said that man's science has outgrown his morality. I should like to give this judgment a new turn and say that our trouble is that our philosophy of man is not in effective control of our science of nature. Thus, when we think of our future in biological terms we are reduced to seeking moral enlightenment from animal societies, making new kinds of men in test-tubes, adapting ourselves to conditions of life not found on our planet, or consoling ourselves for having to remain on it by the discovery of new drugs. None of all this do I wish to condemn. But when we think of the astonishing creativity of man in society, of what he has done in the last few millennia—of the invention of speech and writing, of the foundation of the family and the state, of the evolution of religion, law, and morality, of the so recent appearance on earth of the

137

literature, art, and music, without which life would now seem shorn of attraction, and of science, whose partial validity is shown by its effectiveness, and whose potential for good or evil holds the world in suspense, perhaps then we may feel that no one science, nor even science alone, gives us so rich a promise for the future as the study of the whole achievement of human society. For this study perhaps philosophy is still the best available word.

REFERENCES

1. On this subject see the excellent study of Hernán Rodríguez, *Psicologia y Cibernetica*, Buenos Aires, 1958.
2. J. S. Haldane, *The Sciences and Philosophy*, London, 1929.
3. Mario Bunge, *Causality: The Place of the Causal Principle in Modern Science*, Harvard, 1959.
4. In his *De Nostri Temporis Studiorum Ratione* (1708). See G. Vico, *Opere*, ed. F. Nicolini, Milan, 1958, p. 184.
5. Quoted from Howard Selsam, *Philosophy in Revolution*, London, 1958, p. 95.
6. Gordon Childe, *Social Worlds of Knowledge* (Hobhouse Memorial Lecture), O.U.P., 1949, p. 23.
7. 'The Evolution of Society', *Antiquity* XXXI, 1957.
8. Lucien Febvre, *La Terre et L'Evolution Humaine*, 2nd ed., Paris, 1924, p. 438.
9. Emile Durkheim, *Sociologie et Philosophie*, Paris 1951, p. 141.
10. Morris Ginsberg, *Sociology*, London, 1931, p. 242.
11. Jean Przyluski, *L'Evolution Humaine*, Presses Universitaires de France, Paris, 1942, pp. 20-25.
12. G. Révész, *The Origin and Prehistory of Language*, London, 1956, pp. 35 and 217.
13. *De Natura Deorum* II, 60.
14. Collingwood, *The New Leviathan*, 6, 41; and cf. Révész, op. cit., p. 103.
15. Ernst Cassirer, *Language and Myth*, Dover Publications, pp. 24, 28, and 8 (Originally published in German as Number VI of the *Studien der Bibliothek Warburg*).
16. Hannah Arendt, *The Human Condition*, Chicago, 1958.
17. *Créer*, Paris, 1943, p. 249.

S. A. BARNETT

Communication in Animal and Human Societies

Just as parts of biology have to be built on physics and chemistry, so some aspects of sociology must be based on biology. The interaction of nature and nurture underlies much of social science, as it does biology: hence social scientists should be familiar with the principles of genetics.[13] The study of societies similarly demands an understanding of concepts from the sciences of behaviour: for instance, 'instinct' and 'motivation'. This entails an extensive and up-to-date acquaintance with the work of psychologists and ethologists. (Ethology is the scientific study of animal behaviour.) Biologists should therefore try to make their work in these fields accessible both to their colleagues in the social sciences and to their fellow citizens generally. What follows is an attempt to do this for some items from recent work on communication in our own and other species.

MEANINGS

The word 'communication' in its origins was bound up with the ideas of community and obligation. The root is believed to be the Sanskrit *mei*, to barter. From this follows the meaning of something one ought to give in exchange for something received. In Latin *munis* is an adjective referring to one who does his duty; *munia* are duties, especially those of a magistrate. *Communis*, however, means held in public, by contrast with *proprius*, one's own. *Communicare* was originally to to make something common, to divide or to share it, and this is the origin of our word, 'communicate'. This meaning, or a derivative of it, is implied in the phrase, 'he doesn't communicate', implying some form of social maladjustment.

But today, if communication is mentioned in a scientific context, we think of engineering or mathematics or, in zoology, perhaps of

139

a rather mechanistic account of social behaviour in animals. This sort of use reflects the new demands on language made by those who make and apply new knowledge. It also illustrates the way in which new concepts are introduced and made acceptable by comparison with what is familiar. In the same way, the word 'inform' has the early meaning of 'put into shape'. and later 'inspire', or imbue another with feeling; but now it also means 'tell'; and today information for an engineer—or even an ethologist—is what is communicated and may be defined in mathematical terms. Indeed, in some writings 'information' has been converted (some would say perverted) to mean the reciprocal of the variance of a series of measurements:

$$I = \frac{1}{\sigma^2}$$

Engineers, then, have used words that originally described human behaviour for processes that go on in wires or pipes or valves. And biologists have turned round and tried to grab the words back again, in the hope that the laws and concepts of physics will help them to explain the behaviour of the organisms they study. And not only behaviour: it is now becoming usual to speak of the 'information store' in the chromosomes of egg and sperm as the basis of heredity; and, more obviously, the nervous system is sometimes described in the language of communication engineers. Human communication (using the term in a colloquial sense) always depends on imagery, comparisons and parables. Whether the drawing of these particular analogies will, in any given field, turn out to be much more than an amusing parlour game will depend on whether it leads to fruitful hypotheses.

SOCIAL SIGNALS

All the various biological phenomena which are sometimes said to involve the passage of information are connected by a particular sort of causal relationship. They all depend on *signals*. A signal may be defined, not very precisely, as a small amount of energy or substance which brings about a large change in the distribution of energy or material in a system. This definition does not require action at a distance. In social behaviour both the source of the signal and the system influenced are animals, and the individual receiving the signal substantially increases or reduces its energy expenditure as a result. This is possible because there are amplifying and damping systems in the body of the animal.

Signals are not sharply distinct from other sorts of causes of behaviour. Consider the huddling together during sleep of a group of

animals of the same species. This may sometimes have a heat-con-
serving effect involving a relatively large amount of energy; but
huddling may also be a response to bodily contact acting as a social
signal.[3]

Some of the best known of recent researches on social signals in
animal behaviour are those of N. Tinbergen and his school.[24] These
studies describe animals behaving 'automatically' and in a stereotyped way to well-defined patterns of stimulation. A male three-
spined stickleback (*Gasterosteus aculeatus*) in his territory attacks,
or at least makes certain formal movements towards, another male;
he also responds, in just the same way, to a cigar-shaped object of
similar size, provided it has a red belly. Similarly he courts a crude
model of a female, provided the underside is swollen in the same way
as the belly of a female full of eggs. In other species comparable
analyses have been made of relationships between parent and offspring:
a herring gull chick will peck at a model beak as if it were that of one
of its parents bearing food: the model evokes pecking most efficiently
if, like the original, it is yellow, with a red spot; the colour of the head
to which the beak is attached is of no importance. This sort of quasi-
mechanical response to specific *Gestalten* has been utilised in the
evolution of the cuckoo: the cuckoo chick, with large gaping beak,
provides a highly effective stimulus releasing feeding-behaviour in
its foster-parents; the latter disregard the fate of their own offspring,
however pathetic.

In some instances stereotyped behaviour has been shown to appear
in animals which had been reared in isolation from members of their
own species. The machine works, despite previous inexperience. So
we have a picture of a creature developing, not only the structures
characteristic of its species, but also the behaviour patterns, or rather,
arrangements of the nervous system, which determine that the animal
shall move along the right track as soon as the proper lever is pulled:

Not a bus, not a bus, but a tram.

The preceding paragraphs are of course an exaggeration, even of
the most over-simple accounts of 'innate' behaviour. For one thing,
a particular activity depends usually not only on a specific external
stimulus but also on the internal state of the animal: a stickleback
courts or fights only in spring (when the endocrine secretions are at a
particular level). There are many ways in which the motivation to
perform stereotyped acts can be varied. More important, one is never
justified in assuming that the ability to perform one of these patterns
is independent of experience. The classical definition of 'instinctive

K   141

S. A. Barnett

behaviour', which we can find in the chapter on 'instinct' in the *Origin*,[5] includes the criterion that the behaviour, or at least the ability to perform it, develops independently of individual experience. But we know now that many actions, which have all the superficial appearance of being 'instinctive', do in fact depend on a kind of learning process during individual ontogeny.

Outstanding examples, on which very detailed work has been done, come from birds. One is the following response recently studied in detail by W. H. Thorpe and his colleagues. Some young animals, notably ground-living birds such as geese and moor-hens, tend to follow any moving object within a certain size range; once they have experienced such an object they tend to learn to follow it, and given enough practice they become superficially attached to it. This *imprinting* is ordinarily evoked by a bird's parent; but experimentally it may be attached to a man or an inanimate model, and subsequent social behaviour may as a result be considerably disturbed. The process is, however, not irreversible. It has of course attracted the attention of psychiatrists.

Another group of examples comes from work on the development of bird song, by H. Poulsen, and by Thorpe, P. Marler and others.[16, 22] Bird song is a usual means by which naturalists recognise species, and it depends for its biological value on being distinct from that of other species. It is exactly the sort of thing that has usually been called 'instinctive'. Yet in a number of species the production of the typical song depends on a learning process: the young must hear the performances of older birds of their own kind. In ordinary conditions this occurs inevitably in the early life of each individual bird, but it can be prevented by isolating individuals in sound-proof cages.

It is indeed not possible to say *a priori* to what extent any given stereotyped activity will prove to depend on experience. This is well illustrated by the work of A. Seitz on Cichlid fishes of the genus *Astatotilapia*. The males do not recognise the females if they have been reared in isolation from them.[21] In this respect they differ from the stickleback males made so familiar by the writings of Tinbergen.

In all these animals there is evidently a nervous organisation which is very ready to respond to the conditions in which the stereotyped behaviour is appropriate. This is the basis of the concept of the 'innate releasing mechanism' or IRM, referring to a hypothetical arrangement of the central nervous system. The term IRM may be criticised on the ground that stereotyped behaviour is (as we have just seen) often patently dependent on experience for its development; the word 'innate', in fact, begs the question of just how the behaviour develops during the life history of the individual.[15] The stereotyped behaviour

142

patterns of an adult can be shown, by experiment, to be, some more, some less, *labile* in their development[11]: that is, they depend, to differing extents, on specific conditions or stimuli.

All the 'characters' of an organism depend on the interaction of what is laid down at fertilisation with the environmental agencies acting on the individual as it grows. This is the interaction of nature with nurture already referred to. It is especially complex and subtle in the development of behaviour, since nervous systems are organs, not only of response and co-ordination, but also of learning: they are so arranged that *adaptive change* of response is possible. The unremitting responsiveness of the central nervous system to the animal's surroundings is beautifully shown by the now extensive studies of exploratory learning[2]; this type of learning occurs during an animal's 'motiveless' movements about its living space. Experiment shows that during these movements changes must take place in the animal's nervous system, so that on a later occasion the animal can either take the correct route from one point to another or very rapidly learn the best route from a starting point to a goal. This exploratory learning has often been called 'latent learning', because there is no evidence of it at the time of its occurrence. Its study is an example of the sophisticated yet rigorous researches on behaviour going on in some laboratories today—a far cry from the over-simple notions of conditional reflexes or of 'innate' responses which some people fear are all that students of behaviour have yet to offer.

COMMUNICATION AMONG BEES

The most notable achievement in the study of animal societies has been the work of K. von Frisch and his followers on the hive bee (*Apis mellifera*). A worker about to become a food gatherer makes preliminary flights around the hive; these evidently enable it to learn the topography of the neighbourhood—an example of exploratory learning. Later, it visits sources of nectar or pollen. These visits are usually determined by the behaviour of other bees that have already visited them. A bee that comes upon a new source of food returns and performs movements or 'dances' in the hive that convey the nature, direction, distance and abundance of the food. J. B. S. Haldane[8] has expressed the sort of message these dances carry in the following translation: 'nine workers are to fly 560 yards N.E. by E. of the hive to a place with the smell of the drink which I offer you.'

The dances, unlike those performed by Scottish Highlanders or South Sea Islanders, are the same in each community; or, if there is variation (as there is too in the song dialects of some birds), it is small: they are highly stereotyped, and we must assume that each bee has a similarly standardised nervous equipment enabling it to respond appropriately. Further, bee language differs from our own in being iconic: that is, its form resembles the meaning of the message conveyed. Our language, by contrast, is arbitrary in the relations of the symbols to the thing referred to (except in a few cases of onomatopoea). A further account of the special features of human language is given by Hockett.[12]

Let us return to bees, and in particular to the way in which the site for a new hive is determined by a swarm. A few pioneers explore; if one finds a suitable place it returns and dances, perhaps for an hour. Others go out, return and dance too. The result is that several sites may come to be recommended at the same time; parties form and, by continual dancing, try to attract support for the policy they advocate. Some bees cross the floor, until all those dancing are agreed. Then the whole swarm moves off.

The temptation to talk about 'democracy' is obvious. We have already the long-standing and absurd use of the word 'queen' for the only fertile female in a bee colony. What is the major difference of insect societies from those of men? If we were looking at them from a moral point of view, like the writers of the bestiaries, we might say the absence of crime and maladjustment and the extraordinary perfection of the co-operation between individuals. But differences of this sort all stem from a more fundamental one: that the co-operative behaviour of social insects is stereotyped for each species, like the mating and fighting of a stickleback or the behaviour of a cuckoo and its host. In these, as in most animal species, only the details of social behaviour are variable: the main patterns are standardised and highly predictable, at least in the usual range of enviroments of the species. They have evolved, as structures have evolved, and—it must be assumed—at a similar rate. The dances of bees described by von Frisch were observed also by Aristotle two millennia ago; and this points the contrast with man, since human society and communication then differed in a great number of ways from our own. Crime, which is not found in insect societies, is one price we pay for social adaptability.

Are we then obliged to assume that the study of animal communication can give us no help in understanding ourselves? Certainly, it is now usual to emphasise the plasticity of human behaviour, its variability from time to time and place to place—the fact that it is 'culturally determined' in all its aspects. Margaret Mead[17] has written:

The growing child is systematically patterned in every detail, in posture as well as in gesture, in tempo as well as in speech, in his way of thinking as well as in the content of his thinking, in his capacity to feel as well as the forms which his feeling takes.

Nevertheless, I believe there are at least three ways in which zoology can contribute to the study of human communication. First, it can throw some light on behaviour in infancy—a topic of enormous importance for both normal and pathological behaviour in later life. Second, as Darwin implied, it can suggest useful comparisons in the field of motivation or emotion.[6] Third, it can illuminate the dual nature of human communication.

STEREOTYPED BEHAVIOUR IN INFANCY

If we wish to look for traces of stereotyped behaviour in man, it is reasonable to seek it first in infancy. And in fact we find it there. A particularly clear example has been given by R. A. Spitz and K. M. Wolf.[20] They studied 'social smiling'. This is the charming response given by infants in their early months to the sight of a parent or other human being. We all find it attractive; and it has been reported in the United States that mothers who had at first been rather cool towards their offspring often underwent a marked change of feeling when social smiling began: hence this response may be assumed to have survival value. It is fairly stereotyped; and it produces, if not a standard response in the observer, at least a favourable attitude reflected in a willingness to cherish. Social smiling may be regarded as a social signal. Spitz and Wolf moreover found that the smile could be released by presentation of a hideous mask gently waved in front of the infant. The smiling, then, is performed on presentation of a fairly specific *Gestalt*, and does not involve recognition of any particular person. Later, of course, individuals are discriminated, as a result of a learning process, and then behaviour changes strikingly: many small children come to shun strangers for a time. This aspect of learning in infancy is perhaps comparable to imprinting.

A notable recent discussion of infant behaviour has been that of J. Bowlby.[4] Bowlby's aim is to make use of the concents of zoologists in building on the foundation laid by Freud. This is certainly an improvement on either ignoring psychoanalysis or treating the ideas of Freud as the immutable products of divine revelation. Bowlby begins by suggesting that an infant displays certain stereotyped patterns of behaviour, including sucking, crying, smiling and clinging; and that these are quite primary, independent of experience, and exist by virtue of their survival value. The work of Prechtl has now shown that Bowlby might have added head-turning movements in response to a touch on the cheek—movements which aid the child to find the nipple.[19] Later, when the child is mobile, he tends to follow a parent or parent-figure, rather like a gosling.

From the point of view of a biologist today this is not a surprising notion; but it conflicts with the view that all behaviour is determined in the first place by certain primary needs: these are the so-called homeostatic needs, such as hunger and the maintenance of a particular skin temperature. These needs certainly stimulate some behaviour, such as crying; and other stereotyped activities depend on the internal state for the readiness with which they are performed: for instance, head-turning is more readily evoked in a hungry infant. But this principle does not hold uniformly. The tendency of a well-fed infant to suck between meals is familiar. Still more obviously, 'social smiling' is nothing to do with hunger (or with 'wind', as was once proposed); it is an independent response to a particular visible pattern.

STEREOTYPED NEEDS

We cannot, then, properly interpret infant behaviour wholly in terms of the immediate effects of the homeostatic needs. Further, it is now realised that a list of these needs does not exhaust all that an infant requires from his parents. There are also 'non-homeostatic' needs; and before we continue with Bowlby's argument, it will be useful to look more closely at these additional needs, especially those related to communication. Sucking, crying, smiling and clinging are all means of conveying information to a parent; and the parent in turn caresses and talks and sings to the child, as well as feeding him. Are these subsidiary activities important? Certainly, cuddling a baby—provided he is kept warm somehow—does not serve any of the homeostatic needs. Yet recently it has come to be suggested that contact with other human beings is of profound importance in infancy—and indeed at other ages.

This notion comes partly from studies of laboratory animals. If laboratory rats (*Rattus norvegicus*) are regularly stroked by an experimenter each day early in life, they are later better at learning to run mazes and, what is more important, they grow better, resist 'stress' better and are less 'emotional'.[14] In societies of wild rats 'amicable' intentions are signalled by contact stimuli, such as mutual grooming.[3] Still more remarkable is the work of H. F. Harlow on infant monkeys (*Macacca mulatta*).[9] These animals display a

146

profound disturbance of behaviour if they are separated from their mother even for a brief period; but this can be prevented if they are given a substitute in the form of a kind of tailor's dummy, of suitable shape and texture, to which they can cling. Here, then, in communication by touching, is an apparent need which is certainly not 'homeostatic' in the usual sense of that term. This is another example, from the field of 'motivation', of the way in which psychologists are freeing themselves from excessively simple, 'mechanistic' accounts of behaviour.

Of course, we must not apply these observations too readily to ourselves. The forms and frequency of cutaneous stimulation vary greatly in different human societies. It is not conventional for adult men in Britain today to kiss each other; but it is in France. And Englishmen kissed each other in Nelson's time. The men of ancient Greece, whom we rightly so much admire, no doubt did so even more. Nevertheless, even though much of this behaviour is culturally determined, we may suppose that there is an underlying need and tendency common to all human beings.

This is what Bowlby suggests for infancy. His ideas come from observing what happens when a baby of, say, six months to two years, is separated from his mother for some time and provided with no real substitute. This usually happens when a child has to make a prolonged stay in hospital, or is placed in an orphanage. The first stage is one of protest, which lasts from a few hours to more than a week. This is a period of loud crying and evident expectation of the mother's return. Such a simple form of communication is of course quite general among mammals; its biological value is obvious. What is less obvious is the significance of what happens when the separation is prolonged; the child goes through further stages that Bowlby calls respectively despair and denial. A child in the third stage can be won back to a normal relationship with his mother or other people only with difficulty. Evidently, a failure of a particular sort of communication—the sort ordinarily established between mother and child—interferes with the normal development of social behaviour.

If the stage of protest has obvious survival value, what can we say about the stage of denial? If denial is essentially asocial, it must be disadvantageous in social beings such as ourselves. Presumably, the answer is this. In the primitive conditions in which our ancestors were subject to the natural selection process, children separated for long from their mothers must nearly always have died: hence any secondary consequences of separation, occurring in the few children who nevertheless survived, can have had no biological importance. The

147

actual results of prolonged separation, when this is not fatal, evidently represent a type of adaptation to prolonged and painful internal stimuli. A child in the stage of denial often seems placid and well adapted. Thus individual adaptation has been made at the cost of the ability to make normal personal relationships—in fact, of the ability to 'communicate'. This, evidently, is the calamitous result of failure to satisfy a need which is not yet recognised in the text- books.

THE 'EXPRESSION OF THE EMOTIONS'

The communication of simple messages, such as those conveyed by an infant to his mother, has two aspects. The first corresponds to what Darwin called 'the expression of the emotions'; the second is the *response* on the part of another individual. In our own species the response, and indeed signalling generally, involves the comprehension of the state or feelings of another individual, that is, empathy. Objectively, this can be tested by observing whether a person adjusts his behaviour in accordance with the needs of others or, more generally, in accordance with the likelihood of its having any effect.[10] Animals do not usually do this: for instance, an alarm call may be made, quite 'automatically' as we say, even if there are no members of the caller's species within hearing. The fact that one is not always *successful* in adapting one's signals to the requirements of others— a fact no doubt illustrated by this paper—does not contradict the general thesis.

The phrase 'expression of the emotions' suggests something violent: at least, among the most notable examples there are striking changes in the appearance or behaviour of an animal; for instance, when it is prevented from carrying out some consummatory act. But in fact the events referred to by this term include a whole range of appearances, sounds and odours; these reflect the internal state of the animal, and they are often important in communication because they tell others what the performer is likely to do next. A jackdaw gives an alarm call and flies away; a dog adopts a stiff-legged posture with raised hair and then attacks; a female rat emits a specific odour and allows a male to copulate. The effect on other members of the same species is to make them perform either a similar action (giving the appearance of imitation) or a complementary one. Jackdaws hearing the alarm and seeing the flight repeat the call and fly away also; but a male rat smelling a female in oestrus mounts her.

The 'expression of the emotions' is thus interpreted behaviour-istically as change in 'appearance' which reflects change in motivation; and 'motivation' refers to the internal states which accompany readiness to perform particular activities. In this sense expression of the emotions need not have a communicatory value: it may be merely a perceptible by-product of a particular internal state. Some social signals may have originated as mere physiological by-products. D. Morris[18] has drawn attention to the change in the distribution of the blood that takes place during changes in motivation. Blushing and paling occur not only in men but also in some other mammals; and in certain birds the appearance of the eyes may be markedly altered by increased blood supply—as indeed it is in man, as Darwin pointed out. The primary significance of a redistribution of the blood is that it may prepare the body for emergency by increasing the readiness of the somatic muscles for violent action; but the visible changes provide information which is of potential social value. This value is realised, in most species other than our own, only if there is evolved also a nervous organisation which responds to the specific stimulus pattern provided. Thus it happens that a change in colour, or in the degree to which hairs, feathers or fins are raised, may come to be social signals. In our own species, of course, we *learn* to interpret such changes in our fellows: there is no evidence that we can respond appropriately to these appearances until we have learned from situations in which they occur.

Another group of by-products of behaviour have come to have social significance in the course of evolution. When a stereotyped action, such as a courtship display, is interrupted; or when a situation occurs in which two alternative stereotyped activities, such as attacking or fleeing, might equally well be performed; then it may happen that yet another action is carried out, for instance preening of the feathers or nest-building movements. These substitute acts are called displacement behaviour.[23] They have been much discussed elsewhere, and I shall not enlarge on them now; they seem to be analogous to some neurotic behaviour in man.[1] Their role in communication seems to have arisen in the same way as that of incidental changes in appearance. 'Displacement preening' has come to form part of the courtship display in some birds; nest-making movements have come to be a 'threat' signal in sticklebacks. In this regard displacement behaviour is unlike neurotic behaviour, since the latter is usually anti-social or asocial, though it can of course give information about the dispositions of individuals—if only to psychoanalysts.

HUMAN COMMUNICATION

The animal behaviour described above consists of stereotyped action patterns. In our species, as we have seen, fixed patterns are to

149

be found only in infancy. Granted, blushing and paling, dilation of the pupils, trembling and sweating are all stereotyped; nor are they sharply distinct from the complex action patterns of other species. But they represent reflex components of such activities rather than the patterns themselves. What we have in common with other species is not fixed patterns of behaviour but an array of *needs*; and, lacking fixed, 'instinctive' patterns, we learn, gradually, how to satisfy these needs in infancy and childhood and even later. We succeed, sometimes, by extraordinarily indirect means, such as standing up in front of crowds of our own species and making noises which give no directly useful information at all.

These noises we make, and the visible signs that stand for them, are of two kinds. The first are comparable with the signals made by other species: they state intentions or they exhort others to perform some action. The type of human communication that is unique in the animal kingdom is of the second kind: its simplest form is when one reports something done or observed in the past. Haldane has suggested that boasting may have been important in the evolution of human language. Perhaps the earliest form of propositional language was that used by a fisherman describing his catch. Haldane[7] writes:

> A child which asks for food . . . or calls attention to conspicuous objects, is still a little animal. When it begins to tell its mother where it has gone and what it has seen, it becomes a human being. At this stage it begins to develop an ordered memory of the past, and I doubt whether such an ordered memory, as opposed to memories of striking experiences, existed before the invention of descriptive language.

As he says, religious and political communication is largely of the first or pre-human type. Both types are necessary in every human community, however primitive or advanced.

The primitive aspect of language is however pre-human only in its content. Like all the rest of our complex behaviour, it has to be laboriously learnt. If our chairman wishes to tell us how to get from here to the canteen he must not speak in Chinese. In our own species it is only the capacity to learn to speak that is 'innate'. When the Hayes tried to teach a young chimpanzee to speak, she was with great difficulty induced to pronounce the words 'mama', 'papa' and 'cup' in suitable contexts. Their chimpanzee thus resembled a human idiot, using the term in its technical sense. As Haldane[7] has pointed out, we could use it in the sense of the ancient Greeks also: ἰδιώτης. He writes:

As language developed there must have been heavy natural and social selection against those who were congenitally incapable of using it, and much of what we regard as 'human nature' is, in my opinion, the production of this selection.

We return then to the notion of communication as a social duty. It is equally necessary for us to communicate communally observable facts, in the manner attempted by scientists, and feelings and exhortations in the manner of poets and preachers. With a few lapses, this discourse represents an essay in the performance of the first of these duties.

CONCLUSION

To sum up, the work of ethologists and psychologists enables us now to be clearer about the character of both animal communication and human language—and consequently also about 'instinct' in animal and human behaviour. Much of the complex behaviour of animals is stereotyped and species-specific. This certainly holds for the sounds, displays, odours and so forth by which they communicate with other members of their own species, and also for the responses made to these signals. It does not follow that social behaviour patterns develop independently of the environment: sometimes at least normal development depends on the presence of other members of the species during early life. In man, by contrast, there are few stereotyped behaviour patterns in the strict sense: our patterns of movement, above all the sounds we make, vary from one community to another. Only in infancy there are obvious examples of stereotyped 'social signals' in our own species.

In man, for the most part, what is 'innate' is not any nervous organisation for producing stereotyped movement patterns, but certain propensities and certain needs. Idiots excepted, we all have a propensity for talking (and listening), even though it varies greatly in degree between individuals. That we all have needs, for instance for food, is obvious. But some social needs are less evident: for example, a child's needs for actual contact with its mother. The controversies about 'instinct' can now be put aside. Instead we may turn to finding out more about the needs, precisely defined, that we all have in common, and the results of not satisfying them. Such studies, combined with the findings of geneticists, may eventually give a secure biological foundation to the science of society.

151

S. A. Barnett

REFERENCES

The entries below have been chosen in part because they give recent, documented reviews of the subjects covered. Their bibliographies should be consulted for further references to the original work mentioned in the text.

1. S. A. Barnett, ' "Displacement" behaviour and "psychosomatic" disorder', *Lancet* 269, 1955, pp. 1203-1208.
2. S. A. Barnett, 'Exploratory behaviour', *Brit. J. Psychol.* 49, 1958, pp. 289-310.
3. S. A. Barnett, 'An analysis of social behaviour in wild rats', *Proc. Zool. Soc. Lond.* 130. 1958, pp. 107-152.
4. J. Bowlby, 'Separation anxiety', *Int. J. Psycho-Anal.* (in press).
5. C. Darwin, *On the Origin of Species*, London, 1859.
6. C. Darwin, *The Expression of the Emotions in Man and Animals*, London, 1872.
7. J. B. S. Haldane, 'Animal communication and the origin of human language', *Sci. Prog.* 43, 1955, pp. 385-401.
8. J. B. S. Haldane, in *Studies in communication*, London, 1955.
9. H. F. Harlow, 'Basic social capacity of Primates', *Human Biology* 31, 1959, pp. 40-53.
10. D. O. Hebb & W. R. Thompson, in G. Lindzey (ed.), *Handbook of Social Psychology*, Cambridge, Mass., 1954.
11. R. A. Hinde, 'Behaviour and speciation in lower vertebrates', *Biol. Rev.* 34, 1959, pp. 85-128.
12. C. F. Hockett, 'Animal "languages" and human language', *Human Biology* 31, 1959, pp. 32-39.
13. H. Kalmus, *Variation and Heredity*, London, 1957.
14. J. A. King, 'Parameters relevant to determining the effect of early experience upon the adult behavior of animals', *Psychol. Bull.* 55, 1958, pp. 46-58.
15. D. S. Lehrman, 'A critique of Konrad Lorenz's theory of instinctive behavior', *Quart. Rev. Biol.* 28, 1953, pp. 337-363.
16. P. Marler, 'Specific distinctiveness in the communication signals of birds', *Behaviour*, 11, 1957, pp. 13-39.
17. M. Mead, in L. Carmichael (ed.), *Manual of Child Psychology*, London, 1946.
18. D. Morris, 'The feather postures of birds and the problem of the origin of social signals', *Behaviour* 9, 1956, pp. 75-113.
19. H. F. R. Prechtl, 'The directed head turning response and allied movements of the human baby', *Behaviour* 13, 1958, pp. 212-242.
20. R. A. Spitz & K. M. Wolf, 'The smiling response: a contribution to the ontogenesis of human relations' *Genet. Psychol. Monog.* 34, 1946, pp. 57-125.
21. W. H. Thorpe, *Learning and Instinct in Animals*, London, 1956.
22. W. H. Thorpe, 'The learning of song patterns by birds', *Ibis*, 100, 1958, pp. 535-570.
23. N. Tinbergen, ' "Derived" activities', *Quart. Rev. Biol.* 27, 1952, pp. 1-32.
24. N. Tinbergen, *Social Behaviour in Animals*, London, 1954.

TOM BURNS

Social Norms and Social Evolution

THE ANALOGY OF ANIMAL BEHAVIOUR

Colin Cherry has suggested that 'Communication' has become one of the broad, unifying concepts which occasionally arise to counter the centrifugal tendencies of specialist studies. He names sociology, linguistics, psychology, economics, neurophysiology, semiotic, and communication engineering as disciplines in which the notion of communication figures, and we could certainly add zoology. Alternatively, one might say that the word has become a peg on which to hang a whole wardrobe of notions which are too unfashionable, garish, or otherwise unpresentable for use as everyday wear. Mr. Barnett is well aware of the dangers in so convenient a term, and has confined himself to an account of the bearing which studies of animal behaviour and of human behaviour have on each other. Or rather, he has spoken of the bearing which the study of behaviour and communication between animals has on that of men. (This is one communication channel which usually carries one-way traffic only.)

Because my own contribution is intended to specify the crucial differences between social behaviour among animals and among men, it draws largely on evidence from experimental and other studies of human conduct of the kind mentioned by Mr Barnett.

The community of human with animal behaviour we can, I hope, take for granted. It has been a central assumption of experimental psychology for generations, to say nothing of physiology and the biological sciences at large. But when that is said, it has to be added that the return from animal psychology during this century, say, has been disappointingly small, compared with the progress registered in the cognate sciences of physiology and biology, and in human psychology itself.

This may account partly for the rather cool reception so far given

153

by social scientists to recent work in ethology. The reason for this slower progress lies, I suspect, in the very closeness of the link between animal and human psychological studies. The main search seems to have been directed towards finding zoological models of familiar but uncontrollable or inaccessible psychological processes in man. Quite apart, that is, from the usefulness of rats and pigeons as expendable experimental subjects, they have been regarded rather in the light of cheap ready-made analogue computers or similutors, able to provide clear and simplified instrument readings by which we may construe human behaviour. Fortunately, animal behaviour studies are now a firmly established dependency of a senior science. It is not unfair, I think, to underline the contrast, and its consequences, by comparing the studies of Lorenz and von Frisch with the attempt recorded by Hayes[1] to specify modern English as a mode of social communication for chimpanzees.

Analogy-making has been hunted down enough. It would be silly to damn all analogies. A very great deal of what we like to think of as original thinking comes from the recognition, in a series of observations, of patterns familiar in other contexts. And what is more likely than that such similarities are observable in the conduct of men and of other creatures? Nevertheless, enormous damage has been done by social and political thinking—and action—derived from the misapplication of theories first developed in biology. Also, having got the cruder forms of anthropomorphism out of our system, it would be a pity to become subject to a new fashion for zoomorphic behaviourism.

THE NORMATIVE CHARACTER OF BEHAVIOURAL STUDIES

There are, however, connections between the two kinds of study apart from the fact that human beings are animals too; the theoretical terms in which the studies themselves are conducted have something in common. The main ones are very familiar. All studies which have to do with living creatures must take into account something beyond the content and structure of the physical elements which make them up. There are characteristic and distinctive features of internal organisation. Beyond this, the destiny of a living creature is profoundly affected by the context in which its life is played out. In their turn, again, living creatures can and do affect their context, their organic and inorganic environment.

Among other connotations, these circumstances impose uniqueness, identity, on the material fact of individual existence. This means to say that not only do living creatures pursue separate lives, but that they, and their lives, vary one from another. Variation within the same

154

species, or the same genus, is of obvious importance to the zoologist and the geneticist, but variation also affects the conduct of studies in other biological sciences, in medicine, and in the anthropological and social sciences. Even at the level of 'good' investigatory practice, as I. A. Richards has pointed out,[2] the student has to be sure that any particular instance of a class of organisms which he is observing or dissecting is a 'good' one—i.e. is typical of that class, or rather, is *safe* to use as a 'representative specimen'. Moreover, when we come to anthropological sciences, the actual instances of species, of tissue, of structure, of behaviour have to be regarded in practice as though they were cases in declension from an archetype.

The normative character of all biological studies is more obtrusive, more influential in our approach and thinking, when we come to physiology, medicine and psychology. There are some remarks of Bernard Shaw's about the singularity of 'normal' eyesight which come to mind in this connection. Such renderings of 'normative' occur rather low down in the hierarchy of usages to which this term is subjected in the biological and social sciences. This is not to say that the notion is not at that level of the greatest consequence: medically, of course, but in other ways too. Indeed, it is here that the terms pathological and abnormal are used in their most explicit and technical sense. It is at this level that the crucial importance of the new theoretical dimension introduced by the notion of 'normality' makes itself most apparent, just because it can be, and is sometimes, left out of consideration.

NORMALITY, FITNESS AND ADAPTABILITY

Some years ago, I heard Dr Lorenz describe an experiment designed to show that 'imprinting' was a process by which even behaviour so natural and matter-of-fact as getting food was incorporated in an animal's range of activities. The animals were tawny owls, which live on mice and suchlike prey in the wild state. A number of newly hatched chicks were taken and fed throughout infancy, including the likely 'imprinting' period, with a preparation of meal. Later, at the critical stage of the experiment, the young owls, now approaching maturity, were deprived of their accustomed food and live mice were introduced into their cage. The owls died of starvation while mice ran about their cage.

The following year, Dr Lorenz went on, it was decided to replicate the experiment. But this time, although exactly the same procedure was followed, the owls did kill and eat the mice when the critical stage was reached. When he visited the laboratory some time later,

155

Tom Burns

Lorenz discussed the second experiment as a matter of some interest, and found a difference from the first which he thought of prime importance. The decision to repeat the experiment was taken rather late in the year, and there was no chance of getting owl chicks from the laboratory's usual suppliers. There followed a hurried search through the pet shops of the town, and a sufficient number of chicks was eventually collected. Many of them were, however, poor specimens—'runts' was Lorenz' word.

Here we are confronted with 'normal, healthy, fit' specimens dying in an emergency which the 'abnormal, deficient, unfit specimens' survive. What meaning can be attached to the word 'normal' in this kind of connection, when normality spells imprisonment in a pattern of imprinted conduct, and abnormality means freedom to adapt to unprecedented circumstances? It is difficult to avoid the conclusion that 'normality' carried a heavy load of ethical or aesthetic significance.

We should not be misled by the superficial resemblance between the outcome of this experiment and the stories of Irish peasants and Indian villagers dying of starvation rather than eat the unfamiliar relief maize imported for them. From our vantage point we reverse the criteria for normality. We give higher marks for normality to those deviants who were prepared to perceive and follow alternative courses of action and survive. But in other contexts, the potentially lethal character of normality emerges again. The chances of survival in the first World War of subalterns—the carefully-reared, Public School embodiments of the norms of conduct and character specified for the whole nation—were considerably less than those of the Good Soldier Schweiks. And there is the familiar instance in Durkheim of the high rate of suicide among the members of 'moral élites'—the officers of crack German regiments, and Japanese nobles.

SOCIAL NORMS AS BEHAVIOURAL MODELS

The moral élite is a special case, one in which the accepted norms of a society are provided with the appropriate actors and settings for their portrayal in dramatically effective terms, so that they can serve as models of emulation by society at large. Moral élites are created and exist in order to express—to communicate to all members of a society —the norms of morale and conduct upheld by that society. As individual persons, they can be regarded as the diplomats appointed by society to represent itself to itself; from our present point of view, however, they mark the extension of the normalising principle we started with to the point at which physiological, moral, aesthetic and intellectual norms are nowadays publicly enacted by a chosen few,

156

who are suitably rewarded and whose performances nowadays are broadcast by the agency of television, cinema, journalism, and advertising.

We have now moved a step up the hierarchy of meanings of normal which I mentioned earlier. The link between the studies themselves of animal behaviour and human behaviour, it was suggested, was their fundamentally normative attitude to their subjects. What I want to suggest now is that this characteristic is a stylised version of a very general characteristic of communication between men. For the broadcast communication throughout a society of matters so important as beliefs and codes of conduct it may be necessary to provide for their perpetual re-enactment by the most apt performers. In the more general traffic of everyday affairs, we find touch and communicate with other people largely through our own ability to recognise the normal character of the situation we are in, and to call up the behaviour more or less coherently and effectively appropriate in it.

Psychologically, the second half of this notion has become familiarised in the term 'set', which is broadly speaking a tacit hypothesis about the situation confronting one, and the needs for action inherent in it, an hypothesis which may be confirmed by the sequence of events, or denied and immediately amended. What I want to stress now is that the concrete situation itself, the social event involving communication, is conducted in terms of what we recognise to be its 'normal' character.

While we accept, for many purposes, a community between human and animal worlds, we have also, for other purposes, to identify the obvious and manifold differences. According to the particular viewpoint, these may be subsumed under the heading of one or other of the faculties peculiar to man: toolmaking, language, reference to the past, the extragenetic transmission of information and skill. The critical difference which students of animal and human behaviour and communication have to take into account, I suggest, is the peculiar human aptitude for model-making. Social intercourse occurs in terms of model situations, adult members of any society being equipped with a very large repertoire of such models, or norms of behaviour. Indeed, communication, as it is ordinarily understood, is only possible when some degree of consensus exists about what the norms for conduct are.

BEHAVIOUR AS A SELECTION FROM A REPERTOIRE OF MODELS

Kelley[3] reports an experiment in which he was able to manipulate the models framed by the actors in a situation, while holding the

situation constant. In substance, the experiment involved two groups
of four people each. Both groups, together, were first given an intro-
ductory explanation of the task they were to do. After they went to
their own rooms, each group, separately, was given further instructions. This second set of instructions was designed to impress on the
group either that its task was much more important and difficult
than the other's, or that it was comparatively trivial and easy; moreover, this relationship also was represented in terms of subordination
to the other group, or of superiority.

When the experiment proper began, identical sets of messages were
sent to both groups from the intermediate position between the
rooms. So both groups were given the same task in response to the
same messages. These messages, however, were apparently coming
from the other group in the other room. The messages, which
included irrelevancies, complaints, etc. and were delivered at
irregular intervals, were prepared beforehand, and they, and the
time of delivery, were standard for each experimental run.

In examining the results, which were derived from the degree of
success in the task, the content of the written messages written by
each subject, and interviews after the end of each experimental run,
comparison between the high and low status groups was made by
reference to control groups which had not been given the second set
of 'instructions'. Of the two groups, then, the low status subjects
expressed more dissatisfaction with the job. They sent more messages
quite irrelevant to the task. They more often said they would rather
be in the other team if there were a second run. The low status group
complained about their job to the members of the *other* group, the
higher-ups, but the expression of criticism by the high status group
was confined to members of the same group. The low status group
also expressed more confusion about what they were to do than the
high status group, although there was no significant difference in the
actual score of errors. Criticism by high status persons of the other
group was communicated in every case to the other group. Not only
did the low status group criticise their superiors more frequently—
this criticism was sent in many cases only to fellow members of their
own team. Thus two fairly extensive and coherent patterns of
behaviour consistent with norms of conduct attached to superior and
subordinate positions in working communities were set off by a
single—though emphatic—false clue. The situation confronting each
group was identical.

What we are dealing with here is something much more complicated than can be rendered into equivalents of releaser and imprinted
behaviour patterns, just as language is something much more than a

158

complicated version of the noises a hen makes when she calls her chicks, or of the barking of a dog. But the conduct of the members of the groups does show a remarkable affinity for the kind of behaviour which people in our society regard as typical of different status groups in a stratified social organisation. Having accepted the false definition of their position as superior or superordinate participants in this simple, isolated situation, they obligingly exhibit a large array of characteristics perceived by society at large—not, of course, necessarily formulated to explicit, verbal statements—as normal to that position.

This is something different from the familiar notion of the individual being several distinct social persons, the best-known formulation of which is William James's. The individual 'has as many different social selves as there are distinct *groups* of persons about whose opinion he cares. He generally shows a different side of himself to each of these different groups. Many a youth who is demure enough before his parents and teachers, swears and swaggers like a pirate among his "tough" young friends. We do not show ourselves to our children as to our club companions, to our customers as to the labourers we employ, to our own masters and employers as to our intimate friends.' What this experiment, and others like it, does is to show the norms of action as detachable from the situation and setting with which they are, in ordinary social life, identified. Communication, it suggests, while being conducted in language, gestures and other signs, work movements and so on, is also dependent on the consensus of the people involved about the parameters which are to determine the kind of communication their situation warrants. It wasn't the language used by the two groups in Kelley's experiment which was different—it was the content and direction of messages.

FAMILIAR DIFFICULTIES ARISING FROM THE USE OF DISCREPANT BEHAVIOURAL MODELS

This conception of a repertoire of norms serving as a third set of variables, in addition to language (verbal and non-verbal) and situation, may help to explain some of the curious breakdowns which occur in the communications of everyday. It is a generally accepted fact that working organisations—business concerns and factories—operate well below the effectiveness which might be expected of their aggregate resources—and this despite, in many cases, the technical skill, and willingness to do the job for which they are paid, of their members. Some time ago, I asked a group of four people—the manager of a department in an engineering factory, his deputy, and

159

two production engineers—to keep a record of how they spent their time.[4] They did so, using standard schedules which we drew up beforehand, which showed the time an episode took, the subject, the persons communicated with (if any) and whether they were giving or receiving instructions, or giving or receiving information. This went on for five weeks, each person filling in about thirty-three forms a day. Among other things, I compared the records the manager had made of episodes in which he had been talking with one of his subordinates with the record that particular man had made of the same episode. Two-fifths of the cases showed major discrepancies about the subject of discussion. And in nearly half the cases in which the manager had recorded that he gave instructions to one of his subordinates, that subordinate had recorded receiving information only. The number of times when this discrepancy was reversed—the subordinate noting receiving instructions as against the manager saying he issued information—was trivially small.

This, with the other results of this study, was discussed with the people concerned. These discrepancies were acknowledged as responsible for a good deal of recurrent shortcomings in effective operation which the department—like any other—experienced. Yet these people had known and worked with each other daily for many years; they were fully, and more or less equally, competent to deal with the technical requirements of their jobs. They were familiar with the situations and problems they encountered. They knew each other's language.

At the time, I construed these discrepancies as covert attempts by the subordinates to reject their subordinate status. This, I think now, is an over-simplification. The lack of consensus apparent in their records, and acknowledged later, is clearly something involved in the communication between them, and yet cannot seriously be held to apply either to the language used or to their situation and tasks. It applies, I believe, to the system of normal activity of which each thought himself part at the time of these episodes: and there was, between them, a continual oscillation of this model communication system between that of 'leader and subordinates', and that of 'consultative group'.

Everyday life is full of such ambiguities, and we have constantly to review the programmes of action lying immediately before us. This review is not of the open possibilities presented by completely spontaneous or unprecedented action, but of the ways and means available to us in the repertoire of norms with which we have become acquainted through our membership of a society and our location in this or that social milieu. We can, that is, regard society in abstract terms as a population of norms of conduct which act as channels for the traffic of social communication which we experience as actual social life. As the environmental conditions of social action change, so does the relative efficacy of this or that course of action, and it is the ability to choose from a range of possible norms which distinguishes human social action from animal.

MODELS OF ACTIVITY IN WORKING ORGANISATIONS

The fluctuating relationship of agent—norm—programme of action is nicely demonstrated by the classic Bavelas-Leavitt experiment.[5] In this variant of the original Bavelas experiment, five people are seated around a table, separated from each other by wooden partitions. They have a task to perform which can only be done by communicating with each other. It is very simple. Each is given a box of marbles, of different colours—red, yellow, blue, white, green, brown. The boxes, however, only contain five of these six coloured marbles, and each has a different set. This means that one colour, and one only, is held by everybody. Their job is to find out which colour they all hold in common.

To do this, they are allowed to pass written messages to each other, but only by way of prescribed channels. There are slots in the partitions, which can be closed or left open so as to form a variety of communcation networks. The two which concern us are: first, one in which four persons can communicate with the fifth, and he with them, while they cannot communicate with each other; and second, a network in which each can only communicate with the persons on either side of him. After a few preliminary trials to ensure that everybody knows the procedures, the group is given a series of fifteen tests, identical in nature, the common colour being varied in random fashion. The time taken drops quickly until the sixth or eighth test, and by the fifteenth the task is being done in a minute or so. But on both counts of speed and accuracy, the group with a leader shows up far better than the leaderless group.

The earlier experiments ended here, and the members of the team were interviewed. These interviews showed somewhat parallel effects to the Kelley experiment. The 'leader' in group A, kept furiously busy all the time, is quite pleased with the idea of the test, and quite prepared to have another series, to see whether the time could be bettered. The other members of his team are much less enthusiastic, as can easily be seen from the rather bored way they sit around when they have completed their simple job of posting off the report on their 'hand' during the later tests; they glance at their watches, doodle, and

161

Tom Burns

even, in some cases, deliberately sabotage the job by sending false or comic messages; one person wrote all his messages in Spanish. All the members of the leaderless groups tend to be taken up with the whole affair, at the end, and discuss ways they could have bettered their performance; indeed, one of the reasons for their slowness in the tests is that they swop ideas for improving the system of communication. Any suggestion of this kind in the leader group tends to be firmly suppressed by the leader, who has no time to think up novelties himself, and whose response to ideas from the others is 'we're doing fine as we are—you just send me in what you've got'.

In the main experiment, however, the groups carry on for another fifteen tests—thirty in all. At the sixteenth test the marbles in the boxes no longer have clear distinct colours, but are mottled, muddy. The conditions of the experiment are the same: i.e. one and only one colour is held in common. They had to find the one colour which is common to all. The time taken, and the number of errors goes up steeply for both groups. But whereas the leaderless group fairly soon settles down to its previous speed and accuracy, the leader group never does.

This experiment can be—and has been—the foundation of a number of generalisations about the effectiveness of different kinds of organisational structure in conditions of stability and in conditions of change. In the present context, however, it points to the very minor change in the situation required to make very substantial differences in the comparative effectiveness of alternative programmes of concerted action. In turn the effectiveness of one set of governing norms compared with another may determine not only the chances of their own survival as social institutions, but the livelihoods and even the lives of the people who adopt one or the other. For the sake of illustration, let me cite an example from the recent history of technical development.

ORGANISATIONAL MODELS AND SURVIVAL

The most spectacular product of Government organised technology in Britain is radar. A great deal of this success is said, by those who took part in it, to have been due to the way in which the scientists and technologists concerned were able to communicate with the services, who were no less concerned as users. This communication system was very different from that which obtained in Germany.[6]

In Britain very close contact was established at the outset between the people in the Telecommunications Research Establishment and serving officers in the Royal Air Force and officials in the Air

162

Ministry. This system was consolidated at an early stage by the so-called 'Sunday Soviets' instituted by the then Superintendent of T.R.E. A 'Sunday Soviet' was an open meeting held every Sunday in the Superintendent's room to which were invited all senior Air Ministry officials and all Air Staff Officers. The importance of the occasions as a main channel of communication was soon recognised by the Department and the Royal Air Force, and every Sunday brought its 'galaxy of everybody from Air Marshals down'. Differences in rank were obscured or ignored. A particular type of equipment or an operational problem would be selected, and the division leaders and the group leaders on the T.R.E. side would be there to discuss it. There was thus a very intimate personal connection between the people who had the operational knowledge and the problems to face, who saw their men getting shot down, and who themselves flew and got shot down, on the one hand, and, on the other, the people who worked in T.R.E. and who had an intimate knowledge of the scientific techniques and their scope. The result of this was that the laboratory workers got an immediate emotional as well as intellectual appreciation of the pressing operational difficulties, needs and problems which they could not have acquired by any other means. Equally important, the operational people began to acquire notions of the potentialities of the techniques which they could never have got except through meeting the people who had originated them. The rapid application of the techniques to the problems which did take place was made possible by this intimate joining of operational needs with technical possibilities at the top effective level in an immediate, personal, informal way.

In Germany, a great deal of radar development had been done before the outbreak of war and some equipment of an advanced type was in mass production by 1939, but work on development was virtually closed down for a time because it was thought there would be no further need. When the Germans did start up again, they established a Plenipotentiary for High Frequency Techniques. This official established a chain of new research institutions. He also introduced a system of logging all the available laboratory effort not only in his own institutions but in all the industrial firms, the universities and the technical colleges in the country. He then established contact with an official in the Air Ministry corresponding to himself. The Air Ministry official defined specifications of what the Air Force wanted and these went to the Plenipotentiary for High Frequency Techniques. The latter would then consult his list and see which laboratories were unemployed, and he would post off the specification to one of them. The laboratory would thereupon make

163

an equipment designed without any real knowledge of the operational needs and therefore, in many cases, not meeting them adequately. But much more important than these deficiencies was the fact that most of the possibilities were not realised anyway, because the operational people could not envisage the potentialities of the techniques available, nor could the technical people appreciate the problems of the men who were flying machines.

There is no reason to believe that the Germans were technically inferior either in research and development or in production methods, at the crucial period, or that they were lacking in resources. The clue to the strong lead obtained by this country seems to lie in the adoption of a normative pattern for the communication of information which was appropriate to the conditions set and the overriding pressure for rapid technical advance.

The final suggestion, then, is that in human society there exists a large system of patterns for action which serve as guides for effective action and communication. The number of such guides is far greater than the behaviour actually observable in any society at any one time, or in any one individual. Behavioural norms, or the institutions which they compose, must not, therefore be conceived as matrices from which the members of a society receive the impressions which convert them into social persons: we do sometimes talk as though custom, religious beliefs, social organisation and so forth provided a metagenetic constitution for the individual. Nor should we conceive the social system or the culture of a society as a population of modes of conduct and of symbols all maintained in continuous, observable, existence. It is the range of possibilities and the feasibility of choice between them on the one hand, and, on the other hand, the determinate, specified, nature of each possibility which must enter into any conceptual model of human conduct which attempts to explain 'social evolution'.

The genesis and extinction of individual norms, and of the normative systems we call social institutions, is effected by their cultivation, adoption and neglect by men in the pursuit of a greater and greater measure of control over their total environment, physical and social. The characteristic feature of animal behaviour, and of animal communication systems, is that there tends to be a one-to-one ratio between end and means. There are no alternative norms for action in an emergency—or very few—except, possibly, where deviants or abnormal specimens are involved. Change, if it occurs at all, occurs through the lives and deaths of generations. In human affairs, the process of behavioural change can—perhaps rather fancifully—be seen as projected on to the mediate and artificial population of social norms, with occasional lethal consequences for individuals and groups who become caught up in a one-and-one ratio between the ends they pursue and the social procedures available to them.

REFERENCES

1. C. Hayes, *The Ape in our House*, New York, 1951; London, 1952.
2. See discussion reported in *Transactions of Eight Conference on Cybernetics*, 1951. Ed. H. von Foerster, Josiah Macy Jr. Foundation, 1952, p. 57 and pp. 64-5.
3. Harold H. Kelley, 'Communication in Experimentally Created Hierarchies', *Human Relations* IV, 1951, pp. 39-56.
4. T. Burns, 'Direction of Activitiy and Communication in a Departmental Executive Group', *Human Relations* VII, No. 1, 1954, pp. 73-97.
5. H. V. Leavitt, 'Some Effects of Certain Communication Patterns on Group Performance' *Journal of Abnormal Psychology*, XVLI, 1951, pp. 28-50.
6. T. Burns, 'Social Character of Technology, *Impact* VII, 1955. pp. 147-165.

MICHAEL BANTON

The Autonomy of Post-Darwinian Sociology

*(This paper was not read at the Conference. The final address there was
a report upon the discussions prepared by Professor Asa Briggs)*

Darwinism, like most 'isms', was a dogma. In so far as science
knows any authority, it is the judgment passed upon specific researches by the body of scientists qualified in the particular field, who
are able to build upon the results of good enquiries, amending,
developing, and incorporating them into a tradition. The personal
impress of the innovator has to disappear. In sociology, Charles
Darwin's name was used—or misused—to lend weight to an assertion
for which very little supporting evidence could be adduced, namely,
that the phenomena of social life could only be understood in terms
of heredity and selection. The introduction of biological propositions
did not make this theory more 'scientific' than others; nor, for that
matter, was it particularly novel, for the same attempt to formulate
a sociology based upon biological principles is found in a number of
pre-Darwinian writers. Many scientists today are favourably disposed
towards this approach though only a few latter-day social Darwinists
such as Sir Arthur Keith[1] and Professor C. D. Darlington[2] have
attempted to elaborate its implications. The general position is one
known as naturalism: the premiss that human society is part of the
natural world and is ultimately explicable in the same terms as non-
human phenomena. It has been opposed by another extreme position,
that of anti-naturalism, according to which human society is
independent of nature and has to be studied along quite different lines.

The speakers from the biological sciences conspicuously refrained
from adopting a naturalist standpoint. In fact, the only speaker who
saw the relations between the biological sciences and the sciences of
human behaviour in these sharply contrasting terms was Dr Stark.
He maintained that because man is a moral agent as well as an

167

animal, the extension of the theory of natural selection into the human sphere is illegitimate. The laws of nature serve only to delimit an area of freedom, which we know as culture, and within which selection occurs on the basis of values. This distinction of his drew the fire of several speakers, most notably of Professor Hogben. Where could one possibly draw a line dividing nature and human nature? The whole trend of Stark's paper, Hogben protested, was to assume that Ammon, Lapouge and Gumplowicz's biology was all right but that they had not read enough Kant to know in what circumstances it was applicable: whereas the simple truth was that they had got their science wrong!

Hogben's argument destroys the neo-Kantian dichotomy between nature and culture and makes nonsense of the opposed dogmatisms of naturalism and anti-naturalism. We can never know in advance whether or not the critical relationships will be found to be of a particular kind; the only course is to investigate the matter and hold up the results for public criticism. Nevertheless, I doubt if we ought to forget the arguments of men such as Ammon and Lapouge. The relevance of biological principles to the study of society remains a source of much confusion, and some of it is positively dangerous. An examination of social Darwinism helps make clear its errors to the uninitiated and this is of considerable practical importance because such doctrines often lie at the root of ideologies of racial aggression or class arrogance.

THE INDEPENDENCE OF SOCIOLOGICAL AND HISTORICAL PROBLEMS

An excellent example of the Darwinian approach to social relations, alike in the elegance of its deductions and the clarity of its expression, is Sir Arthur Keith's view of racial prejudice. He knew that there were no pure races, but held that nations, by preserving a separate cultural identity, tended to create distinctive biological groups. In this process, prejudice played an important part. Nature, he said, had arranged national and tribal organisation on a competitive basis; each tribe was a team engaged in the eternal struggle to obtain promotion and avoid relegation. Nature's League also had its divisions—racial divisions—white, yellow, brown and black.

> No transfers for her; each member of the team had to be home-born and home-bred. She did not trust her players or their managers farther than she could see them! To make certain they would play the great game of life as she intended it should be played she put them into colours—not of transferable jerseys, but liveries of living flesh, such liveries as the races of the modern

world now wear. She made certain that no player could leave his team without being recognised as a deserter. To make doubly certain she did an almost unbelievable thing. She invaded the human heart and organised it so that her tribal teams would play *her* game—not *theirs*. She tuned the heart of her teams for her own ends. She not only imbued her opposing teams with an innate love of competition and of 'team-work'; she did much more. What modern football team could face the goal-posts unless it developed as it took the field a spirit of antagonism towards the players wearing opposing colours? Nature endowed her tribal teams with this spirit of antagonism for her own purposes. It has come down to us and creeps out from our modern life in many shapes, as national rivalries and jealousies and as racial hatreds. The modern name for this spirit of antagonism is race-prejudice.[3]

There are several objections to this thesis. One that most scholars would consider decisive is that it assumes racial antagonism to be an inherited trait whereas closer investigations of the matter all indicate that group hostilities are socially transmitted. Even if this criticism be set aside and Keith's argument be held to state only the course of long-term trends, it fails to fit the facts. Racial antagonism does not correlate with emergent demographic isolates. Good correlations have been found between individual prejudice and certain types of personality structure; between racial discrimination and certain characteristic social relationships; between the growth of racialist ideologies and the intensity of economic competition between groups identified by racial criteria. Hypotheses of this order have proved fruitful and have each given rise to a series of cumulative investigations. Sir Arthur Keith's view has not produced hypotheses suitable for testing empirically and it is inconsistent with many of the relationships that have been established. It is on these grounds that current social Darwinist assertions must be rejected and not on any *a priori* assertion that biological explanations of human activities are 'absurd, illogical'.

The anti-naturalist doctrine that the human sciences must use methods different from those of the 'natural sciences' often seems to be impelled by a fear of scientific encroachment which derives from a misunderstanding of the nature of scientific enquiry. To oppose the 'humanities' to the 'natural sciences' is to draw a dividing line in the wrong place: it conceals important differences between physical and biological sciences and tends to assimilate such subjects, even those in which one cannot experiment like astronomy, to the model of

169

physics; it conceals the use of scientific procedures in a wide range of humanities such as archeology, linguistics and geography—quite apart from psychology, economics, and so on. It implies that there is a difference of kind where there is only a difference of degree, and it inhibits communication between scholars. If a line has to be drawn anywhere, it is more useful to distinguish between the attempt to solve theoretical problems posed by an event—which is characteristic of science—and the attempt to arrive at a total attitude towards an event, to comprehend it in a view of life—which is characteristic of philosophy.

Sir Arthur Keith's argument is that racial prejudice is essentially a means of isolating racial groups; that it cannot be properly understood unless its evolutionary function is appreciated. There is a tendency here to confuse function with purpose—which Darwin himself did not always avoid[4]—and to say that one function is more important than others, or that it determines them. It is conceivable that racial prejudice might have the evolutionary function that Keith attributes to it, but this does not explain the variations associated with personality structure and types of social relationship. Students of different sciences may study the same objects, but they study different aspects and seek to answer different questions. In so far, indeed, as separate sciences can be distinguished, it is in accordance not with the phenomena they study, but of differences in the kinds of question they try to answer. This elementary point tends to be obscured by the practice of referring to different 'levels' of investigation, implying that the problems of one level can ultimately be reduced to the data of a lower level. It is to be resisted because, to borrow K. R. Popper's words, 'Science cannot start with observations or with the "collection of data". Before we can collect data, our interest in *data of a certain kind* must be aroused: the *problem* always comes first.'[5] Geneticists are interested in genetical problems, zoologists in zoological problems, sociologists in sociological problems; each must solve their problems in their own terms. It is important to study things such as racial prejudice as psychological, sociological, and economic phenomena—perhaps also as biological phenomena—but we must remember that these are only ways of looking at it. Each approach is limited to answering certain kinds of question and none claims to say what racial prejudice 'really is'; science is not concerned with questions of this order.

In the physical and biological sciences it may appear as if the research worker's task is to explain an *event*, but I am doubtful if in fact this can be the case. The research worker is not interested in every characteristic of the event, but only in those relevant to his interest. It would be more accurate therefore, to say that he seeks to explain certain features of the event or to solve certain problems which it presents.

This distinction helps to clarify another aspect of the problem which has also been confused by the contraposition of opposing dogmatisms. 'Human evolution', Professor Ginsberg concluded, 'is continuous with animal evolution as regards both body and mind'. This view was generally accepted by the conference, but the biological speakers, concerned to guard against an uncritical extension of biological conclusions to the social realm, were at times inclined to exaggerate the differences. Thus Professor Hogben stated that 'While there is admittedly a prima facie case for the assumption that other local differences of animal behaviour are finally traceable to differences with the proper province of genetics, there is no such case for the presumption that different patterns of Man's social behaviour are predominantly traceable to the same source'. Any difference that there maybe is, surely, one of degree. Not all problems of animal behaviour are explicable in genetical terms, and recent research has shown that learned behaviour patterns can be transmitted in animal colonies. In both animals and men behavioural instructions are transmitted genetically, but the problem remains of why one set of instructions rather than another is transmitted. The selection of environments by *Drosophila* in Professor Waddington's experiment may have been genetically determined, but the question of why a particular environment suits a particular species is not explicable in genetic terms.

Genetic factors are demonstrably of critical importance to the explanation of certain problems of human behaviour, such as mental defect, but of no significance to others, such as the study of the mother's brother-sister's son relationship as it occurs in many tribal societies. Because sociology is concerned with problems of the latter kind—the implications for behaviour of different ways of organising societies—it does *not* have to be based on biology. Arguments about the relative similarity and dissimilarity of the subject matter of the biological sciences and the sciences of human behaviour are profitless when the important distinctions both between these two groups of subjects and within each of them, are differences in the kind of problem selected.

SOCIOLOGICAL ANALYSIS OF HISTORICAL PROCESSES

How something has come to be what it is, and how it continues to exist are separate problems which it is necessary to differentiate in

171

discussions relating to evolution. For evolution is a unique and irreversible process raising problems of a historical character. This leads Professor Waddington at one point to suggest—if I understand him rightly—that the sociologist should attempt to explain why he finds a variety of divergent cultures within a small region like New Guinea, and others that are more or less uniform over a vast area. This seems to be primarily a historical problem; it would be most difficult to analyse it in general sociological categories. Concepts such as 'culture' and 'society' are useful for making certain broad distinctions, but it has not yet proved possible to develop them as units of analysis. What the expression 'a culture' is to be used to designate remains unsettled.

If the sociologist is to examine the whole course of what is sometimes called 'social evolution' he can do so only be concentrating upon a limited range of facts. They must also be conceptualised in such a way that he can undertake empirical investigations which will bear upon his hypotheses. Sometimes this is easily done. Social life in many underdeveloped countries today illustrates features which must have characterised life centuries ago in what are now considered advanced societies. Technological progress may not be the most important kind of progress, but it is one of the most outstanding characteristics of human history and it can, to a certain extent, be assessed by objective measures. What then, we may ask, are its human correlates? Quite clearly, there must be a variety: some genetic, some physiological, some psychological, some moral. One important set which the sociologist is best equipped to elucidate are those relating to the mode of social organisation. This aspect of their work does not attract very much interest among present-day sociologists, but it may be worth while attempting a sketch to see what analogies exist between biological evolution and the evolution of social systems.

One of the more important traditions in sociological thought has been the concern with the way in which the structure of a social relationship entails certain forms of behaviour on the part of the people who are parties to it: each has his rights and obligations in respect of the other. At the same time, there are social mechanisms to reward conduct which is approved, and to penalise people for neglect of their obligations. As a man moves from one relationship to another he takes on a new status, so that in the course of a few hours he may be involved with other people in respect of a series of statuses: husband, father, neighbour, motorist, employer, creditor, stockbroker, colleague, etc. In different sorts of societies people acquire statuses in different ways: in some a man's more important statuses are ascribed to him by fixed criteria which make little allowance for

172

the variations in ability from one man to another; in others his more important rights and obligations he acquires by voluntarily contracting into particular statuses. This constitutes a rough scale corresponding to a parallel advance in technology. Recent research enables us to refine it considerably.

In traditional tribal societies status is ascribed to people primarily by criteria of descent. A man's obligations *vis-à-vis* others are determined by his seniority among a group of brothers who belong to a segment of a larger lineage of noble, commoner, or perhaps slave, status. Rank, property and land rights are vested in corporate descent groups. Such a status system is relatively rigid, which may indeed be advantageous for a small-scale society with a primitive technology and a hostile environment. But the development of productive technology requires a greater division of labour and therefore more flexible principles of status allocation. The division of labour must in the first place be on a larger scale and there are narrow limits to the size of the group which can be organised on a basis of descent alone. In the second place, technological progress requires that individual skills be utilised and rewarded according to a man's ability on the job and not according to his rank in society. Able individuals must be able to move up the scale and it must be possible to direct resources into new openings. If this sort of flexibility in the status structure cannot be achieved, technological change cannot come about. However, once changes are set afoot they frequently offer material rewards for further change in the direction enabling technical processes to be employed to best advantage.

The extreme case of a rigid status system is that of Hindu caste organisation, but this appears to be a local and aberrant form of organisation compared with the more general sequence of social changes. A better starting point is the small-scale society of the type made familiar by social anthropologists, in which descent is reckoned almost exclusively down one line, either patrilineally or matrilineally. With an increase in social scale such societies show a tendency to develop a centralised administration and an embryonic form of social stratification which permits those who have won the approval of the central authority to be rewarded with a superior standing. With the development of productive technology such societies show a weakening of the emphasis upon unilineal descent as a principle of status allocation, and this has determinate consequences in other parts of the system, such as, for example, the incidence of divorce. Relationships traced through other lines of descent are utilised by people as a basis for association. Rigidity declines and individual choice acquires larger scope. The elementary family breaks away from the

M

descent group to achieve a measure of autonomy, and there is a general transition from individual to collective rights.

In any society statuses are allocated in a variety of ways and change occurs by a gradual shift in emphasis from one set of criteria to another. Descent remains important in all the major known forms of social organisation. In small-scale tribal societies it is conceived in particularistic terms: his being the son of a particular father determines a man's status with reference to his kinsmen, but it is of little relevance in dealing with people who are not his kin. With the increase in scale, descent is generalised by being used as the basis of larger categories differentiated by rank. The fact that a man is the son of a noble then determines his standing with reference to non-kin, whether of royal descent, nobles, commoners, or slaves. This form of social organisation reached a highly developed form in Western European feudalism. Different estates had their perculiar social obligations, their private law, while in some cases only marriages within the estate were recognised. Possibilities of social mobility within estates improved, though divisions between them remained rigid. The racial stratification found in parts of Southern Africa is a modern example of this form of organisation. A dominant factor in the allocation of statuses—especially occupational statuses—is membership of the appropriate 'estate'; this frequently outweighs considerations of the individual's ability to fulfil the requirements of the status and thus does not make best use of the available human resources. The feudal system of closed social strata operated on a set of principles by which a much larger society could be organised than was possible on a basis primarily of descent. It provided the social framework for a more advanced productive process, but it was quite inadequate as a means of organising a society employing capitalist productive processes. Many observers expect the same inadequacy to bring about radical changes in the African case.

Further technological progress has necessitated increased social and geographical mobility to permit the more effective utilisation of individual skills. This has resulted in a system of open social strata, or classes, in which no one social attribute outweighs the others in the determination of class position. There is a much greater flexibility in the means by which statuses are allocated, permitting people to compete for the more valued ones, and to accept or decline certain sets of rights and obligations as they wish. Descent is still important and the fundamental unit of our contemporary class system is not the individual but the family. Nevertheless the means of allocating status have become very much diversified and specialised, while the change has been continuous in a particular direction. At all stages principles of status allocation other than descent, stratification, and contract can be distinguished: in some societies age and sex differences are given particular significance; in others what Sir Henry Maine called 'the principle of local contiguity' is the basis of rights and obligations between neighbours.[6] But it would appear that the importance of these varies with the general shift in emphasis from descent to contract.

The effects of this movement upon a number of spheres of social life can be traced through, step by step. One example of this, which also bears upon the use of sex differences for the allocation of rights and obligations, is the way in which variations in the relationship between husband and wife correlate with the extent to which the elementary family is incorporated in some larger group. In tribal societies where a group of kinsmen together with their wives and dependents live as a single household, the division of labour between the sexes is sharp; husbands and wives seek companionship among age-mates of their own sex; the marital bond is weaker than the tie of common descent. In peasant societies the household may be smaller, but it forms part of a tightly-knit local community; the dividing line between 'men's work' and 'women's work' remains important, and husband and wife do not share so very many common activities. In industrial societies the increased geographical and social mobility removes an increasing proportion of families from their kinsfolk and childhood friends, so that they are less intimately involved in the social network; for companionship and assistance the husband and wife must look more to one another and less to people about them. Such a view of how changes in the status system affect a particular relationship is suggested not by a reconstruction of historical data but by contemporary studies of different forms of social organisation. In particular, when faced with the problem of accounting for variations in the relationship of a sample of married couples living in London, Dr Elizabeth Bott was forced to the conclusion that 'the degree of segregation in the role-relationship of husband and wife varies directly with the connectedness of the family's social network'.[7] Her hypothesis appears to be borne out by studies of the family in African territories where urbanisation is having a profound effect upon traditional norms of the marital relationship.

Thus it appears reasonable to conceive of an evolution of the status system analogous to organic evolution. In both cases it is possible by reference to objective criteria to determine the line of development and therefore to differentiate evolutionary changes from other changes. In both cases it is possible despite the fact that the process as a whole is a unique historical trend.

M*

Is there anything in such a system of ideas, Professor Waddington has asked, which plays the evolutionary role of natural selection? Certainly peoples who develop forms of social organisation permitting them to exploit their technological potentialities most effectively are favoured as compared with those who fail to do so. But to employ the analogy profitably is well-nigh impossible. To consider nations, races, or classes as discrete units subject to the play of selection, leads inescapably back to the sort of theory that was exploded long ago.

Is there then anything corresponding to mutations as sources of variation? When the Indian culture adopts from the British traits such as a taste for cricket, from what standpoint is this an arbitrary introgression comparable to genes fortuitously linked on a chromosome? When such happenings are referred to as 'historical accidents' does this mean any more than that the causes are not of interest to the speaker? Whenever one power acquires dominion over another, members of the subordinate group must master the social skills valued by their superiors if they are to be accepted by them. The social rewards accorded for proficiency at such apparently arbitrary things as cricket are appreciable, and it can be predicted that in the colonial situation sections of the subordinate group will adopt the corresponding values. Even where two groups of sharply contrasting cultures are in contact and items are transferred from the one culture to the other, there can be no sudden mutation. The subordinate group may adopt certain of their superiors' practices, but this must be a selective process from their standpoint because they cannot adopt everything immediately. What they adopt must have some meaning for them, some relation to their experience of the world, and it cannot have the same significance for them as it has for the members of the other group, as the two worlds of experience differ. New social institutions can arise only from the re-shuffling of elements already present.[8]

It would seem, therefore, that biological analogies cannot at present offer sociologists any intellectual short cuts. Their biggest disadvantage, I suspect, is that they distract attention from the crucial role of the research worker's theories in indicating which facts are relevant to this purpose. Some differences of this order are readily apparent: geneticists, so it was said, concentrate upon types of genetic recombinations and have not until recently been greatly concerned about the sources of hereditary variation. We see no mutations in history, as Dr. Bronowski remarked, because we know so much more about it! But even when biologists and sociologists study similar events they conceptualise them differently and their theoretical interests lead them away in different directions.

CONCLUSIONS

One of the reasons for holding the conference was the feeling that communication between students of biology and of society needed to be improved and that, in particular, sociologists might benefit from a consideration of the lessons learned and the theories developed by their biological colleagues. The inference which Dr. Bronowski drew from the juxtaposition of the two fields of enquiry was that whereas Darwin's work had led scientists to locate the pool of potential variability in man's genetic constitution, the study of society had not yet led to the discovery of any pool of simple forms of behaviour which in their various combinations and recombinations would explain the processes of social change. Has Darwin's work helped us to find any such pool? I doubt it. We might rather say that just as the success of the Newtonian method misled many chemists and biologists into the belief that it could be readily transferred to their subjects, so Darwin in bringing new order into biology led sociologists to try and develop their science along lines which proved unrewarding.

Once sociologists stopped worrying about the biological co-ordinates of human behaviour and concentrated upon the social co-ordinates, they initiated a series of enquiries which have proved capable of progressive development. At the present stage any review of current sociological research[9] has to include work done by scholars from neighbouring disciplines because of its empirical relevance to the interpretation of forms of social life in contemporary Britain. Much of the work done from university departments of Commerce, Education, Political Science, Public Health, Social Administration, etc., is of this kind, and its preponderance obscures the distinctiveness of the research interests of the relatively small core of professional sociology. Modern sociologists operate with two chief frames of reference: one is the quantitative analysis of social characteristics illustrated by studies of social mobility, the distribution of property, etc.; the other is the approach from field investigation and the analysis of case material aiming at a theoretical understanding of the implications of structured social relationships for human conduct. The sorts of problem with which sociologists are at present occupied include such questions as the determinants of occupational prestige, the effect of social class differences upon educational opportunity, the influence of social norms upon levels of industrial production, the effect of organisational structure upon communication both within particular firms and in experimentally constituted small groups, the implications of a man's occupational role for his other social roles and the processes whereby he may exchange one status for another,

177

the determinants of social distance in particular relationships, and so forth. Clearly any biological analogies that may later prove of use are more likely to be relevant to a general synthesis than to particular enquiries of this sort. However, the general opinion among sociologists is that our subject has suffered unduly from premature attempts at synthesis and the pressing need is for the prosecution of research in fields closer to ascertainable fact.

I have argued that sociological problems are independent of biological problems and therefore need to be pursued separately. Certain problems, particularly in the sphere of applied science, contain both sociological and biological elements but their existence serves only to substantiate the view of scientific method adopted here. Research in biochemistry has produced some of the most important discoveries of recent years and 'social biology' may prove another important field linking two specialisms. At present, however, it would appear that while some acquaintance with contemporary biology may give the working sociologist a few hints and stimuli, there can be no wholesale transfer of theories. This is not to imply that either kind of enquiry should be pursued in ignorance of what is going on in the other, for more links will be found as our knowledge increases, and in any case the scientist who knows nothing of subjects outside his special field is not likely to be very good at his own job. Contact between different subjects is crucial, but it is fraught with possibilities for misunderstanding: the research worker regularly makes assumptions of which he is unaware and his colleague from another field needs some acquaintance with the philosophy of science if he is to make any true comparison. A concern with these principles of method has been forced upon me by problems of empirical research and my conclusions may not have been worked through to the point where they are capable of any general application. Nevertheless, I think they help us see why it is that an appeal to biological theories for the solution of sociological problems does not solve these problems, and that sociologists will have to elucidate them without the aid of Darwinism.

REFERENCES

1. Sir Arthur Keith, *The Place of Prejudice in Modern Civilisation*, London, 1931; *Ethnos*, London, 1931
2. C. D. Darlington, *The Facts of Life*, London, 1953; also, *The Conflict of Science and Society*, London, 1948, in which we are told 'The fundamental problem of government is one that can be treated by exact biological methods. It is the problem of the character and causation of the differences that exist

among men, among the races, classes, and individuals which compose mankind' (p. 28.)

3. *The Place of Prejudice*, pp. 34-5.
4. Cf. *The Descent of Man*, edition of 1901, p. 941: 'It is to be especially observed that the males display their attraction with elaborate ease in the presence of the females; and that they rarely or never display them excepting during the season of love. It is incredible that all this should be purposeless'.
5. Karl R. Popper, *The Poverty of Historicism*, London, 1957, p. 121.
6. Sir Henry Sumner Maine, *Ancient Law*, London, 1861, Ch V.
7. Elizabeth Bott, *Family and Social Network*, London, 1957, p. 60.
8. Michael Banton, 'The Restructuring of Social Relationships', in *Social Change in Modern Africa*, ed. A. W. Southall, London, 1960.
9. Cf. John Madge, 'Trends in British Sociological Research since 1950', *Trans. Third World Congress of Sociology*, London, 1956, vol. VII, pp. 85-105.

Notes on Contributors

MICHAEL BANTON: Born 1926, Birmingham; studied at London Schoool of Economics; B.Sc. (Econ.), London; Ph.D. (Social Anthropology), Edinburgh. Assistant in Social Anthropology, University of Edinburgh 1950; Lecturer, 1955.
Author of *The Coloured Quarter*, 1955; *West African City*. 1957; *White and Coloured*, 1959.

S. A. BARNETT: Born 1915, Middlesex; educated Magdalen College, Oxford; M.A.; Senior Lecturer in Zoology in the University of Glasgow. Author of many papers on behaviour and on the effects of low temperature on mammalian life; and of *The Human Species* (2nd edn.), 1957; Editor, *A Century of Darwin*, 1959.

J. BRONOWSKI: Born 1908; educated Jesus College, Cambridge; M.A., Ph.D.; Senior Lecturer at University College, Hull, 1934-42; government service 1942-50; at present Director-General, Process Development Department, National Coal Board.
Author of *The Poet's Defence*, 1939; *William Blake: A Man Without a Mask*, 1944; Selection of Blake's poems for the series The Penguin Poets, 1958; *The Face of Violence*, 1951; *The Common Sense of Science*, 1951; *Science and Human Values*, 1956; *The Western Intellectual Tradition*, 1960; and numerous papers in mathematics.

TOM BURNS: Born 1913, London; educated Parmiter's School and J. & E. Bumpus, Ltd.; B.A., Bristol, 1933. Taught in private schools 1935-1939; Friends' Ambulance Unit 1939-1945. Research Assistant, West Midland Group 1945-1949. Lecturer in Department of Social Study, University of Edinburgh, 1949; Senior Lecturer, 1951.
Author of *Local Government and Central Control*, 1956; *The Management of Innovation* (With G. M. Stalker), 1961.

BENJAMIN FARRINGTON: Born 1891, Cork; educated University College, Cork, and Trinity College, Dublin; graduated in Classics, Philosophy, English and later read Law at Queen's University, Belfast; Professor of Classics, Cape Town, 1929-34; Professor of Classics, University College, Swansea, 1936-56.
Author of *Science in Antiquity*, 1936; *Science and Politics in the Ancient*

181

World, 1939; *Francis Bacon, Philosopher of Industrial Science*, 1949; *Greek Science*, 1953.

MORRIS GINSBERG: Born 1889; educated University College, London; F.B.A., M.A., D.Lit., London; LL.D., Glasgow; LL.D., Nottingham; Fellow of University College. Martin White Professor of Sociology in the University of London, London School of Economics, 1929-54; Emeritus Professor, 1954.

Author of *The Psychology of Society*, 1921; *Studies in Sociology*, 1932; *Sociology*, 1934; *The Idea of Progress: a revaluation*, 1953; *Reason and Experience in Ethics* (Auguste Comte Lecture), 1956; *Essays on Sociology and Social Philosophy*: Vol. 1, *On the Diversity of Morals*; Vol. 2, *Reason and Unreason in Society*, 1956.

LANCELOT HOGBEN: Born 1895, Southsea; educated Trinity College, Cambridge; F.R.S., M.A., Cantab.; D.Sc., London. Professor of Zoology, Cape Town, 1927-30; Professor of Social Biology, London, 1930-37; Regius Professor of Natural History, Aberdeen, 1937-41; Professor of Zoology, Birmingham, 1941-47; Professor of Medical Statistics, Birmingham, since 1947.

Author of *The Comparative Physiology of Internal Secretion*, 1926; *Principles of Animal Biology*, 1930; *Nature and Nurture*, 1933; *Statistical Theory*, 1957.

GEORGE SHEPPERSON: Born 1922, Peterborough; scholar of St. John's College, Cambridge; M.A. Cantab. Lecturer in Imperial and American History, University of Edinburgh, 1948; Senior Lecturer 1960. Visiting Professor of History, University of Chicago, 1959. Has lectured in a number of other American universities. Read papers at the Conference on Religious Movements of a Millennial Character at the University of Chicago, 1960. Co-author of *Independent African: John Chilembwe and the Nyasaland Native Rising of 1915*, 1958. Editor of the *Bulletin of the British Association for American Studies*. Gained his interest in the Scottish Philosophy from historical research into Scottish-American relations, particularly from an examination of Thomas Chalmers and his influence in America. Has published a number of articles on Scottish-American themes in learned journals.

J. MAYNARD SMITH: Born 1920, London; M.A. Cantab. (Mechanical Sciences), B.A. Lond. (Zoology); Lecturer in Zoology, University College, London, 1952.

Author of *The Theory of Evolution*, 1958.

WERNER STARK: Born 1909, Marienbad (Czechoslovakia); educated at the Universities of Hamburg, Prague, Geneva and London; Dr. rer. pol., Hamburg; Dr. Jur., Prague; M.A., Edinburgh; Guest Lecturer, Cambridge, 1941-1942; Lecturer in Social Theory, Edinburgh, 1945-1951; Reader in the History of Economic (and Sociological) Thought, Manchester since 1951. Guest Lecturer, at various times, in the Universities of Basle, Zürich, Heidelberg, Princeton, Harvard, Yale and others.

General Editor, *Rare Masterpieces of Philosophy and Science*, 16 Volumes to date; Author of *Ursprung und Aufstieg des landwirtschaftlichen Gross-betriebs in den böhmischen Ländern*, 1934; *Sozialpolitik*, 1936; *The Ideal Foundations of Economic Thought*, 1943 (also Japanese); *The History of Economics in its Relation to Social Development*, 1944 (also Italian, Japanese, Spanish and German); *America: Ideal and Reality. The United States of 1776 in Contemporary European Philosophy*, 1947; *Jeremy Bentham's Economic Writings*, 3 Vols., 1952-4 (shortened version also Spanish); *The Sociology of Knowledge*, 1958 (also German and Japanese); *Social Theory and Christian Thought*, 1959 (also Spanish and German); *Montesquieu: Pioneer of the Sociology of Knowledge*, in preparation; numerous articles and reviews.

C. H. WADDINGTON: Born 1905; educated, Sidney Sussex College, Cambridge; C.B.E.; M.A.; Sc.D., Cantab.; D.ès Sc., Montréal; F.R.S. Lecturer in Zoology and Embryologist, Strangeways Research Laboratory, Cambridge, 1933-45; Professor of Animal Genetics, Edinburgh, since 1947, and Hon. Director, Agricultural Research Council Unit of Animal Genetics.

Author of *Introduction to Modern Genetics*, 1939; *Organisers and Genes*, 1940; *The Scientific Attitude*, 1941; *Epigenetics of Birds*, 1952; *Principles of Embrology*, 1956; *The Strategy of Genes*, 1957; *The Ethical Animal*, 1960.

BASIL WILLEY: Born 1897; educated Peterhouse, Cambridge; M.A., Cantab.; F.B.A.; F.R.S.L.; Hon. Litt. D., Manchester. Lecturer in English at Cambridge, 1923; King Edward VII Professor of English Literature since 1946.

Author of *Tendencies in Renaissance Literary Theory*, 1922: *The Seventeenth Century Background*, 1934; *The Eighteenth Century Background*, 1940; *Coleridge on Imagination and Fancy*, 1946; *Nineteenth Century Studies*, 1949; *Christianity Past and Present*, 1952; *More Nineteenth Century Studies*, 1956.

INDEX

Acheulian 'hand axes', 91
adaption, xiv–vi
Aeneid (Douglas's), 21
Akenside, Mark, 20
Alpine race, 51
Amici, 38
Ammon, Otto, 49, 50, 53, 54, 55, 56
  on Aryan race, cit., 51
*Animals and Plants under Domesti-
  cation*, 40
antiquarian, the, 30
apprentice teaching, 74–5
Aquinas, 7
Aristotle, 6–7, 122–3
Aryan race, 51
Ashworth, Prof. J. H.,
  cit., 28
Ainsworth, W. F., 28
atoms, xix
Augustine, 7
Autobiography (Darwin's),
  cit., 4, 9

Bacon, Francis, 132
Baden, Grand Duchy of, upper and
  lower classes, cf., 51
Barlow, Lady,
  cit., 9
Barzun, Prof. Jacques,
  cit., 29
Bateson, xvi, 74
Bavelas-Leavitt experiment, 161
bees,
  communication among, 143–5
behaviour, 151, 164
  analogy of animal, 153–4
  as a selection from a repertoire of
    models, 157–9
  displacement, 149
  familiar difficulties arising from
    the use of discrepant models,
    159–61

Hogben on, cit., 171
  normative character of studies,
    154–5
  social norms as models, 156–7
  stereotyped, in infancy, 145–6
biology, 65, 155, 170
  constancy and , 91
  history and, 92, 93
  physics and, xx
  sociology and, 64, 77, 78–81, 86,
    91, 101–3, 130, 132–3, 135, 137,
    139, 167–8, 171, 172, 176, 177–8
bird-song, 142
birds, 142
birth, 72
Bismarck, 42
Blache, Vidal de la, 133
Black, Joseph, 18
Blair, Hugh, 19
Boerhaave, Hermann, 22–3
Boltzmann, xix–xx
Bonnet, 8
Bott, Dr Elizabeth, 175
Bowlby, J., 145–6, 147
brain, xiv
  animal, 129–38
Brown, Thomas, 30
Buffon, 8, 9 10
Burns,
  cit., 21
Butler, Samuel, 2, 10, 112
  cit., 2, 3

Cambridge, 20
Carlyle, Thomas, 26
  cit., 20, 27
Cassirer, Ernst,
  on language, cit., 136
Catholicism, 53
Chambers, Robert, 31
Chambers' Encyclopaedia,
  cit., 5